S0-AUQ-133

REGISTRATION CARD

Register immediately to receive these benefits:

▶ Access to our Technical Support Hotline

▶ Receive information on future software updates

▶ Receive information on new Corel products and special offers

Please fill out the following information, or tape your business card here.

First Name

Last Name

Company Name (if applicable)

Job Title

Address

City   State/Province

Country   Zip/Postal Code

Telephone Number with Area Code   Fax Number with Area Code

▶ I will most likely use the following software products with Corel GALLERY:

1. _____
2. _____
3. _____

▶ I purchased Corel GALLERY from:

- ❏ Computer Store
- ❏ Non-computer/Non-book Store
- ❏ Book Store
- ❏ Mail Order
- ❏ Direct from Corel
- ❏ Bundled with other manufacturer's product

▶ How do you classify the business where you work?

- ❏ Small Company (up to 100)
- ❏ Medium (100-500)
- ❏ Large (500+)
- ❏ Home-based
- ❏ Educational/Training Institute
- ❏ Government

▶ What key factor(s) influenced your decision to purchase Corel GALLERY?

- ❏ Friend/Colleague
- ❏ Product Quality
- ❏ Consultant
- ❏ Price/Value
- ❏ User Group Demo
- ❏ Dealer Recommendation
- ❏ Sales Literature/Demo Disk
- ❏ Software Compatibility
- ❏ Magazine Product Review
- ❏ Brand Name
- ❏ Trade Show Demo
- ❏ Other _____
- ❏ Corporate Standard
- ❏ Advertisement

Internationale Addresses
Register Now!

Please return your registration card to the Corel address nearest you.
Write the appropriate address on the registration card.

U.S.A.

Corel Corporation
P.O. Box 3595
Salinas, California
93912-3595
U.S.A.

Deutschland

Corel Corporation
YYZ YOW 700050
Postfach 1862
6090 Rüsselsheim
Deutschland

España

Corel Corporation
YYZ YOW 700050
Apartado 514 F D/28080
28080 Madrid
España

Nederlands

Corel Corporation
YYZ YOW 700051 M01
Postbus 616
2130 Ap Hoofdorp
Nederlands

United Kingdom

Corel Corporation
YYZ YOW 700046 M01
P.O. Box 66
Hounslow, TW5 9RT
United Kingdom

France

Corel Corporation
YYZ YOW 700044 M01
Boite Postale 28
93601 Aulnay-S-Bois Cedex
France

Italia

Corel Corporation
YYZ YOW 700049 M01
Casella Postale 292
20092 Cinisello Ballsamo
Milan, Italia

Worldwide

Corel Corporation
1600 Carling Avenue
Ottawa, Ontario
K1Z 8R7
Canada

COREL

COREL GALLERY™

REGISTRIERUNGSKARTE

Füllen Sie dieses Formular aus, wenn Sie folgende Vorteile nutzen wollen:

▲ Anrecht auf unseren Hotline-Service
▲ Informationen zum Upgrade auf künftige Software-Versionen
▲ Informationen über neue Produkte und Sonderangebote

Füllen Sie bitte die folgenden Felder aus oder legen Sie Ihre Karte bei.

Vorname

Nachname

Name des Unternehmens (sofern zutreffend)

Position

Adresse

Stadt   Staat/Bundesland

Land   Postleitzahl

Telefonnummer mit Vorwahl   Faxnummer mit Vorwahl

▲ Welche Programme werden Sie hauptsächlich zusammen mit Corel GALLERY benutzen?

1.
2.
3.

▲ Wo haben Sie Corel GALLERY gekauft?

☐ Computerhandel ☐ Buchhandel ☐ Direkt von Corel
☐ Weder Computer–noch Buchhandel ☐ Versandhandel ☐ Im Bundle mit dem Produkt eines anderen Herstellers

▲ Wo arbeiten Sie?

☐ Kleine Firma (bis zu 100 Mitarb.)
☐ Mittelgroßes Unternehmen (bis zu 500 Mitarb.)
☐ Großunternehmen (über 500 Mitarb.)
☐ Zuhause
☐ Bildungseinrichtung oder Trainingsinstitut
☐ Behörde

▲ Welche Hauptfaktoren haben Sie bei Ihrer Kaufentscheidung für Corel GALLERY beeinflußt?

☐ Freund/Kollege
☐ Produktqualität
☐ Berater
☐ Preis- Leistungsverhältnis
☐ Software-Kompatibilität
☐ Händlerempfehlung
☐ Messevorführung
☐ Gruppenvorführung
☐ Firmenstandard
☐ Herstellername
☐ Marketingmaterial/Demo-Diskette
☐ Produktvorstellung in einer Zeitschrift
☐ Werbeanzeige
☐ Andere

COREL GALLERY

TARJETA DE INSCRIPCIÓN

Inscríbase de inmediato para aprovechar estas ventajas:

▲ Acceso a nuestra línea telefónica directa de asistencia técnica

▲ Recibir información sobre la futuras actualizaciones de software

▲ Recibir información sobre nuevos productos Corel y ofertas especiales

Complete la siguiente información, o bien fije aquí su tarjeta de visita con cinta adhesiva

Nombre

Apellido

Nombre de la empresa (de ser aplicable)

Cargo

Dirección

Ciudad — Estado/Provincia

País — Código postal

Número de teléfono con código internacional — Número de fax con prefijo

▲ Estos son los productos de software que pienso utilizar con Corel GALLERY:

1.
2.
3.

▲ He adquirido Corel GALLERY:

- ☐ En un establecimiento de informática
- ☐ En una librería
- ☐ Directamente a Corel
- ☐ En otro establecimiento (no de informática ni una librería)
- ☐ Por correo
- ☐ Incluido con el producto de otro fabricante

▲ ¿Cómo clasificaría el lugar en el que trabaja?

- ☐ Pequeña empresa (hasta 100 empleados)
- ☐ Gran empresa (más de 500 empleados)
- ☐ Educación/formación
- ☐ Mediana empresa (100-500 empleados)
- ☐ Trabaja en casa
- ☐ Administración pública

▲ ¿Qué factor o factores clave influyeron sobre su decisión de comprar Corel GALLERY?

- ☐ Amigo/compañero de trabajo
- ☐ Demostración para grupo de usuarios
- ☐ Reseña sobre el producto en una revista
- ☐ Norma de la empresa
- ☐ Calidad del producto
- ☐ Recommendación del distribuidor
- ☐ Nombre de la marca
- ☐ Anuncio
- ☐ Consultor
- ☐ Material de ventas/disco de demostración
- ☐ Demostración en feria de muestras
- ☐ Relación precio/prestaciones
- ☐ Compatibilidad de software
- ☐ Otro

COREL GALLERY

CARTE D'ENREGISTREMENT

Vous devez être enregistré pour:

▲ Appeler notre ligne de Support technique

▲ Bénéficier de mises à jour pour les futures versions

▲ Être informé de produits et d'offres spéciales

Merci d'indiquer les renseignements suivants

Prénom

Nom

Société (le cas échéant)

Titre

Adresse

Ville

Pays — Code Postal

Téléphone — Fax

▲ J'utiliserai probablement les logiciel suivants avec Corel GALLERY:

1.
2.
3.

▲ J'ai acheté Corel GALLERY?

- ☐ Chez un revendeur
- ☐ Dans une librairie
- ☐ Auprès de Corel
- ☐ Autre magasin
- ☐ Par correspondance
- ☐ Associé à un autre produit/matériel

▲ A quelle catégorie appartient l'entreprise où vous travaillez?

- ☐ Petite entreprise (<100 sal.)
- ☐ Grand entreprise (500+)
- ☐ Enseignement/Formation
- ☐ Moyenne entreprise (100-500)
- ☐ Artisan/Travail à domicile
- ☐ Services publics

▲ Quel sont les facteurs qui vous ont décidé à acheter Corel GALLERY?

- ☐ Ami/Collègue
- ☐ Démo Groupe utilisateurs
- ☐ Article dans magazine
- ☐ Choix de l'entreprise
- ☐ Qualité du produit
- ☐ Conseil d'un revendeur
- ☐ Nom de la marque
- ☐ Publicité
- ☐ Consultant
- ☐ Brochure/Disquette démo
- ☐ Démo salon
- ☐ Qualité/Prix
- ☐ Compatibilité du logiciel
- ☐ Autres

 **© Corel Corporation, 1994**
Corel **GALLERY** Clipart Catalog - Version 1.0 (First printing)

3G Graphics, Inc. 206-774-3518

Archive Arts 619-723-2119

Cartesia Software..609-397-1611

Image Club Graphics, Inc., Calgary Alberta 403-262-8008

One Mile Up, Inc..703-642-1177

TechPool Studios..216-382-1234

Totem Graphics Inc. 206-352-1851

Phone: 613-728-8200
Fax: 613-728-9790

PRINTED IN CANADA
Q046-GAL

Path =Clipart\Category\vendor\sub-category

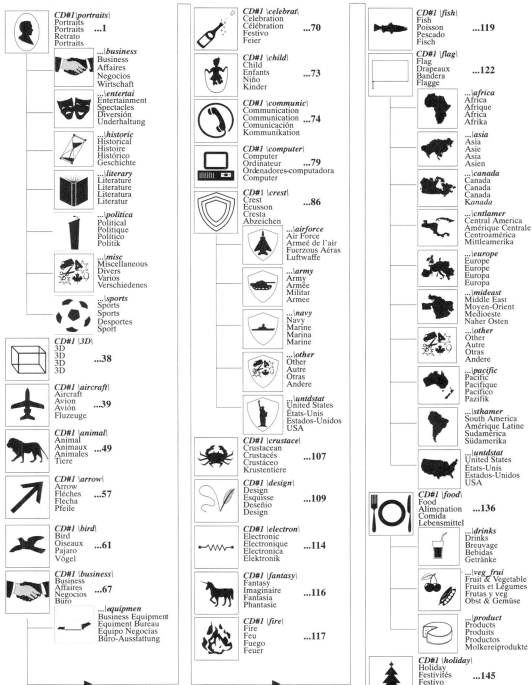

CD#1 \portraits\
Portraits
Portraits ...1
Retrato
Portraits

...\business
Business
Affaires
Negocios
Wirtschaft

...\entertai
Entertainment
Spectacles
Diversión
Underhaltung

...\historic
Historical
Histoire
Histórico
Geschichte

...\literary
Literature
Literature
Literatura
Literatur

...\politica
Political
Politique
Político
Politik

...\misc
Miscellaneous
Divers
Varios
Verschiedenes

...\sports
Sports
Sports
Desportes
Sport

CD#1 \3D\
3D
3D ...38
3D
3D

CD#1 \aircraft\
Aircraft
Avion ...39
Avión
Fluzeuge

CD#1 \animal\
Animal
Animaux ...49
Animales
Tiere

CD#1 \arrow\
Arrow
Fléches ...57
Flecha
Pfeile

CD#1 \bird\
Bird
Oiseaux ...61
Pajaro
Vögel

CD#1 \business\
Business
Affaires ...67
Negocios
Büro

...\equipmen
Business Equipment
Equiment Bureau
Equipo Negocias
Büro-Ausstattung

CD#1 \celebrat\
Celebration
Célébration
Festivo ...70
Feier

CD#1 \child\
Child
Enfants ...73
Niño
Kinder

CD#1 \communic\
Communication
Communication ...74
Comunicación
Kommunikation

CD#1 \computer\
Computer
Ordinateur ...79
Ordenadores-computadora
Computer

CD#1 \crest\
Crest
Ecusson ...86
Cresta
Abzeichen

...\airforce
Air Force
Armeé de l'air
Fuerzous Aéras
Luftwaffe

...\army
Army
Armée
Militar
Armee

...\navy
Navy
Marine
Marina
Marine

...\other
Other
Autre
Otras
Andere

...\untdstat
United States
États-Unis
Estados-Unidos
USA

CD#1 \crustace\
Crustacean
Crustacés ...107
Crustáceo
Krustentiere

CD#1 \design\
Design
Esquisse ...109
Desénio
Design

CD#1 \electron\
Electronic
Electronique ...114
Electronica
Elektronik

CD#1 \fantasy\
Fantasy
Imaginaire ...116
Fantasia
Phantasie

CD#1 \fire\
Fire
Feu ...117
Fuego
Feuer

CD#1 \fish\
Fish
Poisson ...119
Pescado
Fisch

CD#1 \flag\
Flag
Drapeaux ...122
Bandera
Flagge

...\africa
Africa
Afrique
Africa
Afrika

...\asia
Asia
Asie
Asia
Asien

...\canada
Canada
Canada
Canada
Kanada

...\cntlamer
Central America
Amérique Centrale
Centroamérica
Mittleamerika

...\europe
Europe
Europe
Europa
Europa

...\mideast
Middle East
Moyen-Orient
Medioeste
Naher Osten

...\other
Other
Autre
Otras
Andere

...\pacific
Pacific
Pacifique
Pacífico
Pazifik

...\sthamer
South America
Amérique Latine
Sudamérica
Südamerika

...\untdstat
United States
États-Unis
Estados-Unidos
USA

CD#1 \food\
Food
Alimentation ...136
Comida
Lebensmittel

...\drinks
Drinks
Breuvage
Bebidas
Getränke

...\veg_frui
Fruit & Vegetable
Fruits et Légumes
Frutas y veg
Obst & Gemüse

...\product
Products
Produits
Productos
Molkereiprodukte

CD#1 \holiday\
Holiday
Festivités ...145
Festivo
Feiertage

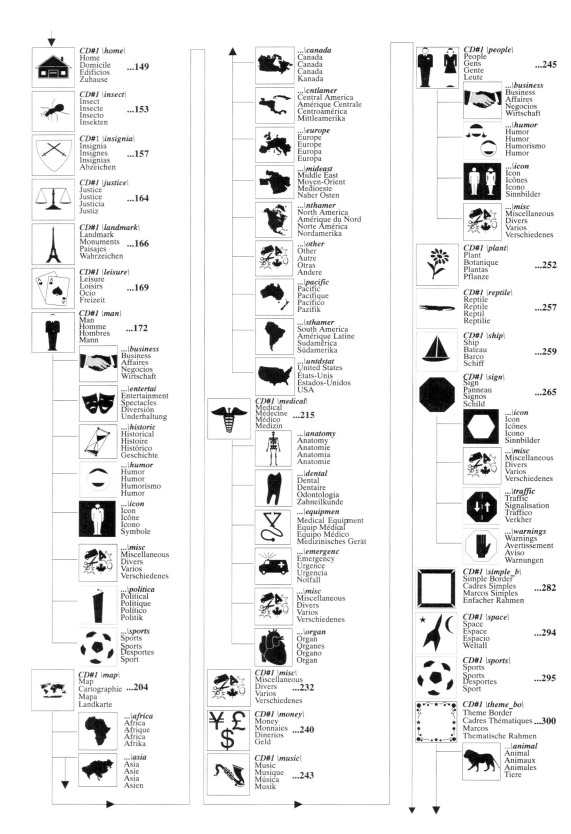

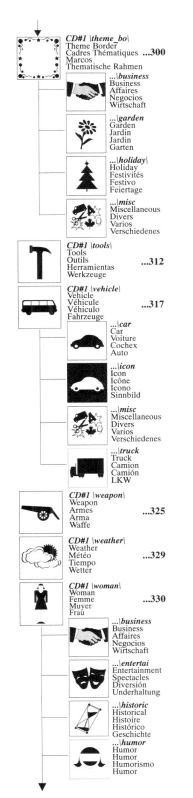

CD#1 \theme_bo
Theme Border
Cadres Thématiques **...300**
Marcos
Thematische Rahmen

...\business
Business
Affaires
Negocios
Wirtschaft

...\garden
Garden
Jardin
Jardin
Garten

...\holiday
Holiday
Festivités
Festivo
Feiertage

...\misc
Miscellaneous
Divers
Varios
Verschiedenes

CD#1 \tools
Tools
Outils
Herramientas **...312**
Werkzeuge

CD#1 \vehicle
Vehicle
Véhicule
Véhiculo **...317**
Fahrzeuge

...\car
Car
Voiture
Cochex
Auto

...\icon
Icon
Icône
Icono
Sinnbild

...\misc
Miscellaneous
Divers
Varios
Verschiedenes

...\truck
Truck
Camion
Camión
LKW

CD#1 \weapon
Weapon
Armes **...325**
Arma
Waffe

CD#1 \weather
Weather
Météo **...329**
Tiempo
Wetter

CD#1 \woman
Woman
Femme **...330**
Muyer
Frau

...\business
Business
Affaires
Negocios
Wirtschaft

...\entertai
Entertainment
Spectacles
Diversión
Underhaltung

...\historic
Historical
Histoire
Histórico
Geschichte

...\humor
Humor
Humor
Humorismo
Humor

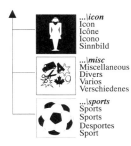

...\icon
Icon
Icône
Icono
Sinnbild

...\misc
Miscellaneous
Divers
Varios
Verschiedenes

...\sports
Sports
Sports
Desportes
Sport

Portraits
Portraits
Retrato
Portraits

Business
Affaires
Negocios
Wirtschaft

abekawa l

agnelli l

aikawa l

akers l

alexand l

allen_p l

alley_w l

amorm_a l

anders l

angus l

aoi l

araskog l

arman_g l

artzt l

attali l

azcarag l

barad_j l

barnevi l

barrows l

bartz_c l

bass_an l

bauman l

benettn l

benshof l

bentonp l

berlusc l

betenct l

birkn_d l

blackc l

bloodwr l

bonfiel l

bossidy l

bourke l

bowen_j l

brainrd l

Portraits
Portraits
Retrato
Portraits

Business
Affaires
Negocios
Wirtschaft

brooksa l

brown_h l

bsh_aug l

buffet l

buntroc l

burke l

bushnel l

callowa l

cannavi l

carseym l

cassini l

chao_e l

chazen l

chung_s l

clintnh l

coen_i l

cole_jn l

collins l

coors_p l

coperma l

cowplnd l

coxchmb l

crandal l

cyr l

davis_m l

dejouan l

dell l

derklug l

desimon l

dieter l

dill_b l

drexler l

eamerr l

eaton l

eguhi l

Portraits
Portraits
Retrato
Portraits

Business
Affaires
Negocios
Wirtschaft

ejiri l

elliot l

erhard l

evans_r l

feruzia l

feruzif l

fireman l

forbesj l

fourtou l

gambino l

gamblek l

gates l

gates_b l

gates_r l

gelb_r l

gerber l

gestner l

gill_d l

girombl l

glass l

gledhil l

godoffa l

goizuet l

goldsmi l

gomez l

gotti_j l

greenbe l

haberer l

hahn_t l

hamada l

hammr_a l

hanson l

hariman l

hart_pt l

hashida l

Portraits
Portraits
Retrato
Portraits

hass l

hayami l

hayasak l

hearstw l

hefner l

hefnr_c l

heinz l

helu_sl l

hemsley l

henders l

herst_r l

hewlett l

hilger l

hilton l

horn_k l

hortonr l

iacocca l

imura l

ito l

jaffre l

jhnsonb l

jobs l

jones_j l

josefsn l

ju_yung l

junkins l

k_shing l

kahn l

kaizaki l

kapor l

karan_d l

kasakss l

kawai l

kawamot l

kay_ash l

Portraits
Portraits
Retrato
Portraits

Business
Affaires
Negocios
Wirtschaft

kearns l

kessler l

kinnear l

klein l

kluge l

kngslyp l

kong l

koplvit l

koplwtz l

kraver l

kroc_j l

kuehler l

kume l

kurasaw l

larsen l

laudere l

lauren l

laybrng l

lazarus l

luciano l

luiso_a l

mahoney l

makihar l

malonej l

manzi l

marcusb l

mark_re l

marshal l

maucher l

maxwelh l

maxwell l

mcdermo l

mcdonel l

micheln l

miles_m l

5

Portraits
Portraits
Retrato
Portraits

Business
Affaires
Negocios
Wirtschaft

millercl

mital

miyazakl

moor_dnl

mor_takl

morit_al

murdochl

nakamurl

nasul

natorijl

nesbitll

noordal

nortonpl

onasisrl

oreillyl

packardl

perelmal

perotl

pfeiffel

platerzl

poe_shrl

polingl

poncetl

price_bl

purvesl

quinlanl

quinnjbl

raab_gkl

rawl_lwl

redstonl

reedl

roach_jl

rokfeljl

rosenbel

rosenfll

6

Business
Affaires
Negocios
Wirtschaft

ross_s l

roth_jo l

rothsch l

sainsbr l

saito l

sandrsj l

scharp l

schreye l

schwab l

scully l

sekimot l

sells_h l

shanker l

shiki l

shugart l

siebert l

simmons l

sinklrr l

smale l

smith_l l

stearnp l

steel_d l

steinbr l

stempel l

stiritz l

stone l

strenge l

suzuki l

tashima l

tellup l

thoma_d l

thomasr l

thompso l

tish_l l

tonseth l

Portraits
Portraits
Retrato
Portraits

Business
Affaires
Negocios
Wirtschaft

toyoda 1

trump_d 1

vagelos 1

valenti 1

vecchio 1

vecci 1

vernon1 1

vpierer 1

vreelnd 1

vwachem 1

wadaula 1

waltona 1

wang_bo 1

weill_s 1

weiss_w 1

welch 1

wethers 1

whitmor 1

wolf_st 1

wood_j 1

woolard 1

wozniak 1

wygod_m 1

yamaji 1

yung_jo 1

ziff_wi 1

Portraits
Portraits
Retrato
Portraits

ab_iman l

abdul_p l

adams_b l

alda_a l

allen_t l

altma_r l

andersn l

anderso l

andrews l

aplegat l

arquett l

arsenio l

ashly_e l

assante l

atnbr_d l

axlrose l

aykroyd l

bachara l

baez_j l

baker_a l

bakula l

baldwin l

baldwnb l

barkn_e l

bartnel l

barymor l

baryshn l

basinge l

beattyw l

belafon l

bening l

bennett l

bergen l

berle_m l

Portraits
Portraits
Retrato
Portraits

Entertainment
Spectacles
Diversión
Underhaltung

bernrds1

berry_h1

biset_j1

black_c1

bly_rob1

bogguss1

boltn_m1

bono1

boone_p1

boosler1

bostwic1

bowie1

bradl_e1

brinkle1

brokw_t1

brooks1

brosnan1

brown_b1

brown_j1

brown_m1

brwne_j1

brysonp1

bufet_j1

burke_d1

burnett1

burns_g1

burton11

butlery1

cage1

caine_m1

campbel1

cann_ja1

capshaw1

carey_m1

carln_g1

Portraits
Portraits
Retrato
Portraits

Entertainment
Spectacles
Diversión
Underhaltung

carp_mc l

carroldl

carson l

carterc l

carterd l

carvey l

cash_jo l

cesar_s l

chambrr l

chapman l

chase_c l

child_j l

chung l

clapton l

clark_d l

clese_j l

close_g l

cockerj l

cole l

colinsj l

collinj l

collinp l

collnsg l

connery l

coperfi l

coppola l

corbett l

cosby l

costner l

cox_c l

crawfrc l

crennar l

cronkte l

cronynh l

11

Portraits
Portraits
Retrato
Portraits

Entertainment
Spectacles
Diversión
Underhaltung

cruise l

crystal l

curic_k l

curts_j l

danson l

danza_t l

davis l

davis_g l

davisju l

day_dor l

demorna l

deniro l

denuve l

denverj l

dep l

dern_l l

devto_d l

dey_s l

diamon l

dillerp l

dillon l

dimondn l

doglasm l

doherty l

dolly l

domingo l

donahue l

donalds l

douglsk l

downeyr l

downs l

dreyfus l

dryfus l

duke_p l

Portraits

Portraits
Retrato
Portraits

Entertainment
Spectacles
Diversión
Underhaltung

eastwoo l

elonz_h l

english l

estefan l

estevez l

etaylor l

evans l

evansd l

everlyd l

everlyp l

fabares l

falk_p l

farrowm l

fields l

fishr_c l

fonda_b l

fonda_j l

ford l

ford_fa l

foster l

fox_mic l

gabor_e l

gabor_z l

garci_j l

garr_t l

gayle_c l

geffend l

geraldo l

gere_r l

gibsonm l

gifford l

gil_vin l

gilbrtm l

givens l

Entertainment
Spectacles
Diversión
Underhaltung

glovr_d l

goodman l

gordy_b l

grammer l

grant_a l

greeneg l

greer_g l

griffit l

grifinm l

grifith l

grodinc l

gumbel l

guthrie l

hackman l

haggard l

hall_dr l

hamltng l

hancock l

hanks l

hannah l

harelsn l

haris_e l

harmn_m l

harrisn l

hart_m l

hartmn l l

hary_db l

hawn_g l

hemng_m l

henly_d l

hennr_m l

hepbrnk l

hndrsnf l

hoffman l

hoganp l

Portraits
Portraits
Retrato
Portraits

Entertainment
Spectacles
Diversión
Underhaltung

hopebob I

hopkins I

horne I

howrd_r I

hunt_he I

hurt I

hustn_a I

iglesas I

irons_j I

jackee I

jacksnk I

jackson I

jacs_la I

jacsona I

jaffe_s I

jagger I

janet I

jenings I

jenning I

jillian I

johns_d I

jones I

jones_g I

jones_j I

judd_w I

juli_ra I

julia_r I

k_kelly I

keaton I

kensi_p I

kidmann I

king_bb I

king_dn I

king_la I

kirstie I

Portraits
Portraits
Retrato
Portraits

Entertainment
Spectacles
Diversión
Underhaltung

kline_k l

koppelt l

kristof l

ladd_c l

lange_j l

lansbry l

laroque l

lavin_l l

lawrenc l

leach_r l

lee_mch l

lee_spk l

lemmon l

lenojay l

lenox_a l

leterma l

lewis_r l

liza l

loklear l

lovett l

lowe_ro l

lucas_g l

lucci_s l

lunden l

lynn_lr l

macgrwa l

maclach l

maclain l

madonna l

malkvch l

mandrel l

manilow l

margrta l

marin_c l

marshll l

Portraits
Portraits
Retrato
Portraits

Entertainment
Spectacles
Diversión
Underhaltung

marti_s l

martnez l

mason_j l

mathisj l

matln_m l

matthau l

mccartn l

mcentir l

mcferri l

mckay_j l

mclaghl l

mcmahon l

mcneil l

medvd_m l

michael l

midler l

miler_d l

millerb l

mofat_d l

moore l

moore_d l

morgn_l l

morrisn l

moyersb l

murphy l

musburg l

nair_m l

nash_gr l

nelsnct l

nelsonw l

newhrtb l

newmanp l

newtonj l

newtonw l

nicholm l

nichols l

nielsen l

nolte_n l

norvile l

o'boyle l

oconnor l

oconorc l

olin_le l

olsen_k l

oneal_t l

oneil_e l

ono_yok l

ophrah l

ovitz l

pacinoa l

palmerr l

patrc_j l

pauleyj l

pavarot l

pen_tel l

penn_s l

perez_r l

perry_l l

pesci_j l

pfeifer l

philbin l

phili_c l

philipj l

philips l

picasso l

plimptn l

pollock l

porzkov l

Portraits

Portraits
Retrato
Portraits

povich l

powerss l

preslye l

preslyp l

prestly l

preston l

price l

prince l

pryor_r l

purcels l

quaid l

quin_ai l

quin_an l

raitt_b l

raphael l

rather l

redford l

reinr_c l

rem_ l

reynold l

richard l

richrdl l

ritchie l

river_j l

robards l

robbins l

rogers l

rogersk l

rogersr l

ronstad l

roseane l

ross_d l

rosseli l

rourke l

russell l

Portraits
Portraits
Retrato
Portraits

Entertainment
Spectacles
Diversión
Underhaltung

ryan_m l

ryder_w l

safer l

sagansk l

saget_b l

santana l

sap_car l

saradon l

sawyerd l

schiffe l

schwrtn l

scorses l

scott_w l

sedakan l

segal_s l

selleca l

selleck l

seymorj l

shae_jh l

shandli l

sharif l

shatner l

sheen l

shepard l

sherida l

shields l

short_m l

shriver l

silverr l

simon l

simon_c l

simon_p l

simonsg l

sinatra l

sinfeld l

Portraits
Portraits
Retrato
Portraits

Entertainment
Spectacles
Diversión
Underhaltung

 COREL

skaggs l

skelton l

smith_h l

smith_w l

smithja l

smoth_d l

smoth_t l

somer_s l

sophia l

space_s l

speling l

spielbe l

springs l

stack_r l

stahl_l l

stalone l

stamos l

star_ri l

stevens l

stewart l

stewrtj l

ston_ol l

ston_sh l

straigh l

streep l

streisa l

stuat_m l

stwartp l

stwartr l

sutherl l

swayze l

tandy_j l

taupinb l

taylorb l

Portraits
Portraits
Retrato
Portraits

Entertainment
Spectacles
Diversión
Underhaltung

tesh_j l

tharp_t l

thick_a l

thoma_m l

thomasj l

tilis_p l

travi_r l

trebe_a l

tritt_t l

tune l

turne_j l

turne_t l

ueberot l

urich l

van_she l

vandame l

vandros l

vandykj l

vanilla l

victori l

vila_bo l

wagnr_l l

walkr_p l

wallace l

walsh l

walters l

ward_sl l

waren_l l

warwick l

washden l

waterst l

watly_j l

weaver l

weavr_s l

weber_a l

Portraits
Portraits
Retrato
Portraits

Entertainment
Spectacles
Diversión
Underhaltung

wendt_g l

white l

whitney l

whoopie l

wil_mon l

wilderg l

wiliamj l

wiliams l

willi_m l

william l

willis l

winger l

winingh l

winkler l

winters l

wodward l

wonders l

woodard l

woodruf l

woods_j l

wriht_r l

wynette l

xuxa l

yankvic l

yanni l

yokumd l

young_n l

young_s l

yrwoodt l

zefire l l

Portraits
Portraits
Retrato
Portraits

Historical
Histoire
Histórico
Geschichte

adams_j l

adamsjq l

andropv l

arthur l

ashe_a l

asimo_i l

astaire l

atwater l

babbage l

ball_l l

bartonc l

benguri l

buchanj l

cage_j l

cagneyj l

churchi l

clevela l

cole_na l

coolidg l

crawfrd l

crosb_b l

czar_ni l

da_vinc l

davis_b l

davis_j l

davisjr l

degaull l

disny_w l

disrael l

duch_wi l

duke_wi l

einstei l

eisenho l

f_d_r l

Portraits
Portraits
Retrato
Portraits

Historical
Histoire
Histórico
Geschichte

fillmor l

fonteyn l

ford_he l

franco l

frankln l

gable_c l

gagarin l

gandh_m l

gandhii l

gardnra l

garfiel l

garland l

georg6_ l

gillesp l

gleasnj l

grang_r l

grant_c l

grant_u l

groucho l

hampton l

harding l

harrisb l

harriso l

hayes l

hendrix l

hepbrna l

hooverh l

hudsn_r l

j_f_k l

jacksna l

jeffers l

johnson l

joplinj l

kenedyr l

Portraits
Portraits
Retrato
Portraits

Historical
Histoire
Histórico
Geschichte

khomeni I

krushch I

I_b_j I

lenin I

lincoln I

macarth I

madison I

malco_x I

mckinle I

meir_gl I

michlan I

monroej I

napoleo I

nureyev I

piercef I

polk_jk I

rasputn I

rockefl I

rosevel I

sakharo I

taft I

taylorz I

teddy_r I

tojo_hi I

tolstoy I

tracy_s I

truman I

tse_tun I

tyler_j I

v_buren I

wang I

warhola I

washing I

Portraits
Portraits
Retrato
Portraits

Historical
Histoire
Histórico
Geschichte

wayne_j l

welk_l l

wilsonw l

yamamot l

Portraits
Portraits
Retrato
Portraits

Literature
Literature
Literatura
Literatur

bombeck l

bradsha l

caroloa l

chancel l

clancey l

cooke l

daniele l

hubbard l

king l

krantz l

mailer l

martinj l

michenr l

rushdie l

sagan_c l

sheehyg l

sheldon l

vidal_g l

Portraits
Portraits
Retrato
Portraits

Political
Politique
Político
Politik

 COREL

akihito l

andru_c l

andrw_p l

anne l

antall l

aquino l

arafat l

arens_m l

assad l

baker l

banks_d l

bayh_ev l

bentson l

biden l

bingama l

blackmn l

bonoi_d l

boothro l

boxr_ba l

bradley l

brady_n l

bran_cm l

bransta l

brownje l

brownro l

brwn_ha l

bryan_r l

buchana l

buckley l

burdick l

burns_c l

byrdrob l

caldron l

calejas l

campb_c l

Portraits
Portraits
Retrato
Portraits

Political
Politique
Político
Politik

  COREL

capertn l

carlson l

carolin l

carterj l

casto_f l

chafee l

chamorr l

charles l

cheney l

chils_l l

clintnb l

clinton l

cochran l

craig_l l

cristia l

cuomo l

danfort l

deconci l

deklerk l

delor_j l

diana l

dingall l

dinkins l

dodd_c l

dquayle l

drenber l

duchess l

duglash l

e_dole l

edith l

emir l

endar_g l

englerj l

ershad l

exon_j l

Portraits
Portraits
Retrato
Portraits

Political
Politique
Político
Politik

feinstn l

finey_j l

florio l

foley_t l

ford_j l

ford_we l

frank_b l

frnklnb l

g_bush l

garrett l

gephard l

ghali_b l

gingric l

glenn_j l

goldind l

gorby l

gore_al l

gortari l

gramm_p l

grasley l

green_b l

greensp l

grosvno l

grove l

harkin l

havel_v l

heath_e l

helms_j l

hohenzl l

huseink l

inuye_d l

jaggerb l

jesse l

jibri_a l

karager l

Portraits
Portraits
Retrato
Portraits

Political
Politique
Político
Politik

kasebau l

kempjac l

kenedjr l

kenedya l

kenedyj l

kenedyt l

kerybob l

king_br l

kirkpat l

kisseng l

kngfahd l

kohl l

krapray l

kuwait l

lautenb l

leahy_p l

levin_g l

levy_d l

lott_tr l

macdon l

mack_co l

macmill l

mandela l

mankill l

marshlg l

mcain_j l

mcconel l

means_r l

michlmn l

miler_z l

mitchll l

miteran l

miyazaw l

molinag l

mosbach l

Political
Politique
Político
Politik

 COREL

moyniha l

mubarak l

mulrone l

murth_j l

mutalib l

narasim l

nazarba l

nelsn_b l

nixon_r l

noriega l

north_o l

novello l

nunn l

nussl_j l

owens_w l

parks_r l

peng_li l

perez l

princep l

princsm l

q_noor l

qaddafi l

queen_e l

queen_m l

r_dole l

rabin_y l

rafsanj l

ramos_f l

reagan l

regle_d l

renquis l

riegled l

roberts l

robinso l

romer_r l

Portraits
Retrato
Portraits

   COREL

rostenk l

roth_wi l

ruutel l

sadam_h l

saud_pr l

scali_a l

schroed l

schwarz l

shamir l

sharona l

shevard l

simonps l

simpson l

siner_g l

smith_b l

solzhen l

souter l

stephan l

stevenj l

stevent l

strauss l

sullivn l

sundln l

sung_k l

symingt l

templ_b l

thatchr l

thomas l

thurmon l

tsongas l

turnert l

voinvic l

walesa l

waltrsd l

weicker l

Portraits
Portraits
Retrato
Portraits

Political
Politique
Político
Politik

weld_w l

whit_by l

whitten l

wilder l

wilsn_p l

wilsonh l

wofford l

won_shk l

woo_r_t l

xiaopng l

yeltsin l

yeutter l

zenawim l

Portraits
Portraits
Retrato
Portraits

Sports
Sports
Desportes
Sport

aaron_h l

agasi_a l

alomarr l

andre_m l

andrett l

andrt_j l

atisano l

baugh_s l

becker l

bird_ll l

boggs l

borg_bj l

bradsht l

brett_g l

canseco l

Portraits
Portraits
Retrato
Portraits

Sports
Sports
Desportes
Sport

capriat l

carew_r l

chamber l

clemens l

connerb l

conors l

cosell l

couples l

courier l

earnhar l

edber_s l

ekersly l

elway_j l

everet l

everson l

ewing l

fitipal l

foreman l

foyt l

goodin l

graf_s l

gretzky l

griffey l

grubr_k l

gsoccer l

hamil_d l

hamilts l

hardawy l

hendrsn l

hogan_b l

holms_ll l

holyfie l

hull_br l

jacksnb l

jordan l

Portraits
Portraits
Retrato
Portraits

Sports
Sports
Desportes
Sport

joynr_f1

kelly_j1

kin_bj1

laver_r1

lemieux1

lemond1

luyendy1

maas1

magic_j1

malon_k1

mansell1

maricha1

marino1

mattngl1

mays_wi1

mccovey1

mcenroe1

mears1

messier1

mitchel1

montana1

mullinc1

navrati1

newcomb1

nicklau1

palmr_a1

patrese1

petty_r1

playerg1

prost_a1

pruet_s1

robinsd1

robnsoj1

rocket1

rodrigu1

Portraits
Portraits
Retrato
Portraits

Sports
Sports
Desportes
Sport

rose_p l

russelb l

ryan_no l

rypie_m l

sabatin l

sampras l

sanders l

seles l

senna l

snead_s l

stern_d l

stocktn l

strawbe l

sulliva l

thoma_i l

tildn_b l

trevino l

tyson_m l

unser_a l

vincent l

wade_vi l

watsn_t l

wilandr l

witt_k l

yamaguc l

arrow3d1	arrow3d2	check3d1	check3d2	cir3d
cross11	cross12	diam3d	hex3d	money3d
octgn3d	outl3d1	outl3d2	outl3d3	outl3d4
outl3d5	outl3d6	oval3d1	oval3d2	pent3d
sqbtn3d1	sqbtn3d2	sqbtn3d3	sqbtn3d4	sqbtn3d5
star3d	symb394	symb395	symb595	symb596
tri3d	x3d			

747	airball	apollo16	atlantis	balloon1
balloon3	beech_f	beech_s	beech_t	biplane1
biplane2	blimp	bomber	c_47	cessna
colshut	columbac	dc_all	f16	float
flyboat	fokker	glider	hawker	helcop1
helcop2	helcop3	jet1	jet2	jet3
jet4	l_1011	mallardc	plane	plane372

Aircraft
Avion
Avión
Fluzeuge

plane373

plane374

plane375

plane376

plane377

plane378

sat1

sat2

ship371

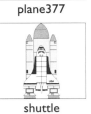
shuttle

skorskyf

skorskys

skorskyt

skylab

skylab1

skylabc2

symb241

symb242

symb259

symb393

symb478

symb514

symb515

symb532

takeoff

vulcan

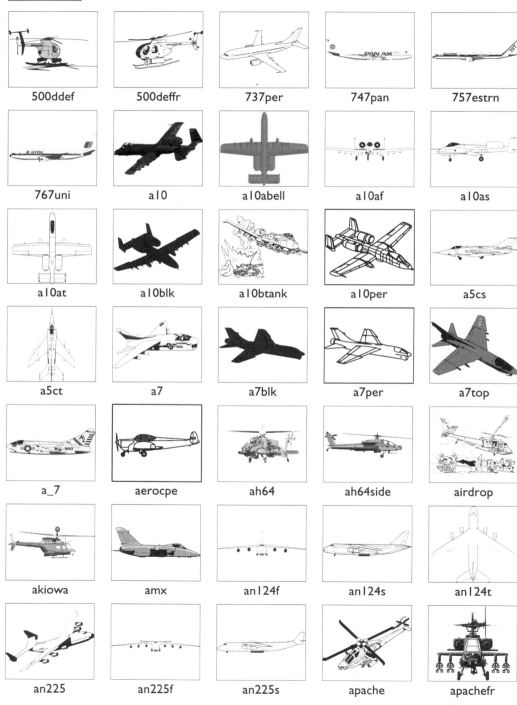

500ddef	500deffr	737per	747pan	757estrn
767uni	a10	a10abell	a10af	a10as
a10at	a10blk	a10btank	a10per	a5cs
a5ct	a7	a7blk	a7per	a7top
a_7	aerocpe	ah64	ah64side	airdrop
akiowa	amx	an124f	an124s	an124t
an225	an225f	an225s	apache	apachefr

Aircraft
Avion
Avión
Fluzeuge

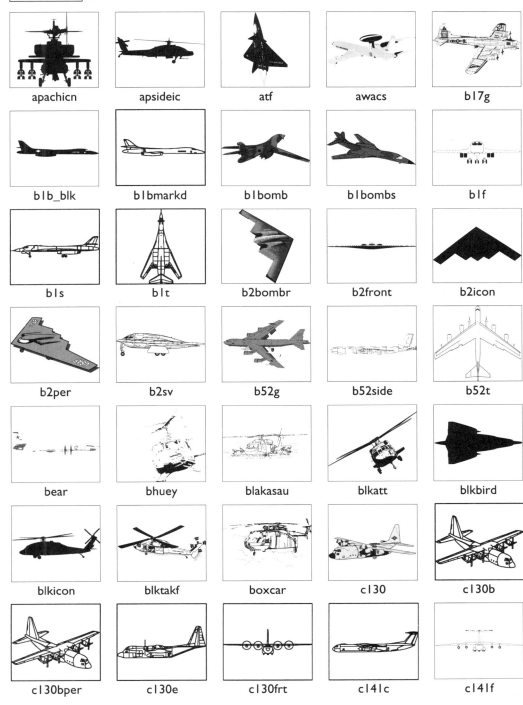

apachicn	apsideic	atf	awacs	b17g
b1b_blk	b1bmarkd	b1bomb	b1bombs	b1f
b1s	b1t	b2bombr	b2front	b2icon
b2per	b2sv	b52g	b52side	b52t
bear	bhuey	blakasau	blkatt	blkbird
blkicon	blktakf	boxcar	c130	c130b
c130bper	c130e	c130frt	c141c	c141f

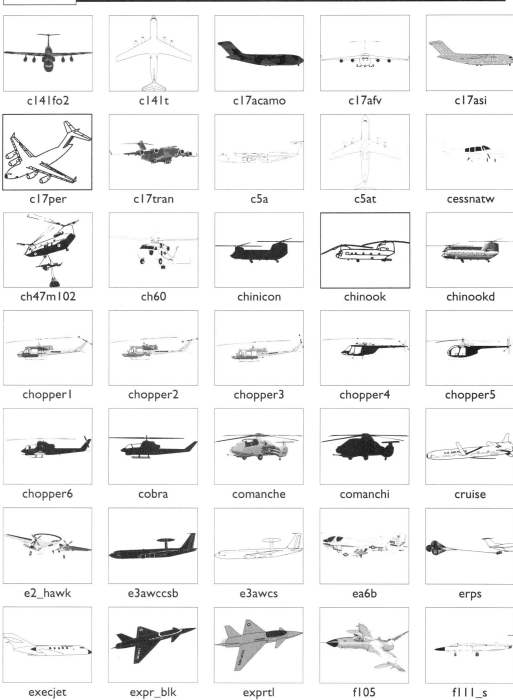

c141fo2	c141t	c17acamo	c17afv	c17asi
c17per	c17tran	c5a	c5at	cessnatw
ch47m102	ch60	chinicon	chinook	chinookd
chopper1	chopper2	chopper3	chopper4	chopper5
chopper6	cobra	comanche	comanchi	cruise
e2_hawk	e3awccsb	e3awcs	ea6b	erps
execjet	expr_blk	exprtl	f105	f111_s

Aircraft
Avion
Avión
Fluzeuge

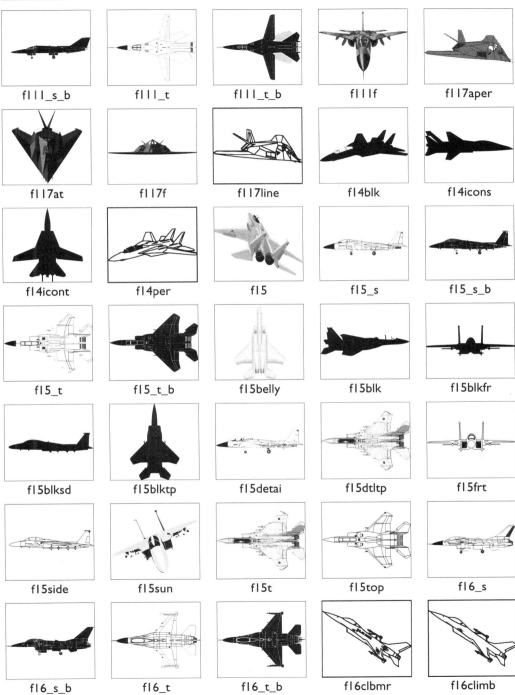

f111_s_b	f111_t	f111_t_b	f111f	f117aper
f117at	f117f	f117line	f14blk	f14icons
f14icont	f14per	f15	f15_s	f15_s_b
f15_t	f15_t_b	f15belly	f15blk	f15blkfr
f15blksd	f15blktp	f15detai	f15dtltp	f15frt
f15side	f15sun	f15t	f15top	f16_s
f16_s_b	f16_t	f16_t_b	f16clbmr	f16climb

Aircraft
Avion
Avión
Fluzeuge

f16dtl

f16dtlsd

f16dtltp

f16front

f16grysd

f16mrksd

f16side

f16toff

f16top

f16tpblk

f16up

f16upblk

f18icons

f18icont

f22

f22f

f22t

f4

f4ef

f4hpha

f86

f_14dtl

f_14per

f_14side

f_14top

f_18dtl

f_18per

f_18side

f_18top

fishbed

gulfblk

gulfstr

harrf

harrfv

harrier

Aircraft
Avion
Avión
Fluzeuge

headup

heavydep

heavydrp

helcopt1

helcopt2

helcopt3

hh3e

hormone

huey

hueyhor

hueyigep

hueyresc

hueysimp

hueytop

ils

intruder

jagf

jags

jas39gr

jas39s

jayhawk

jeticon

jeticon1

jeticon2

jeticon3

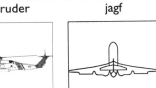
jeticon4

jump

kc10

kc10at

kc130

kiowaic

l1011tw

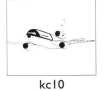
m2000sic

md11per

md80amer

46

Aircraft
Avion
Avión
Fluzeuge

one mile up inc

mig21f	mig21s	mig21t	mig23f	mig23t
mig25	mig25frt	mig25ss	mig25top	mig29
mig29ss	mig29t	mig29top	migclimb	migside
mira	mira2000	miraclim	mohawk	mohowkic
mrange	nasp	osprey	ospreyo	ov10bf
ov10bt	phantom	phntmblk	seacobra	seaknigh
seasprit	simul	skr_sk	skr_sk_b	skytrain

Aircraft
Avion
Avión
Fluzeuge

sr71a	stlth_bm	su19	su19blk	su25tic
su27	su27s	su27side	su27top	tacamo
tbird	thndrbrd	tigero2	tornado	tornatsv
tornattv	tu126	tu160f	tu160s	tu160t
tu22f	tu22s	tu22t	uh60	wkiowa
wright	wrightf	x29	zonejump	

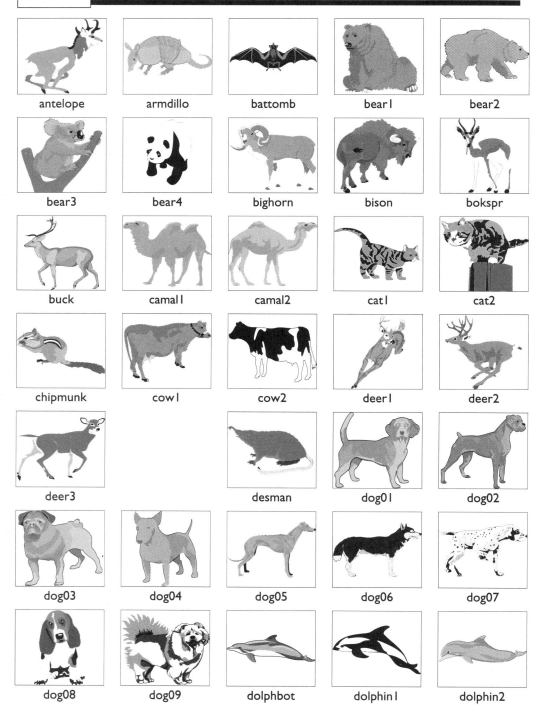

antelope	armdillo	battomb	bear1	bear2
bear3	bear4	bighorn	bison	bokspr
buck	camal1	camal2	cat1	cat2
chipmunk	cow1	cow2	deer1	deer2
deer3		desman	dog01	dog02
dog03	dog04	dog05	dog06	dog07
dog08	dog09	dolphbot	dolphin1	dolphin2

Animal
Animaux
Animales
Tiere

 COREL

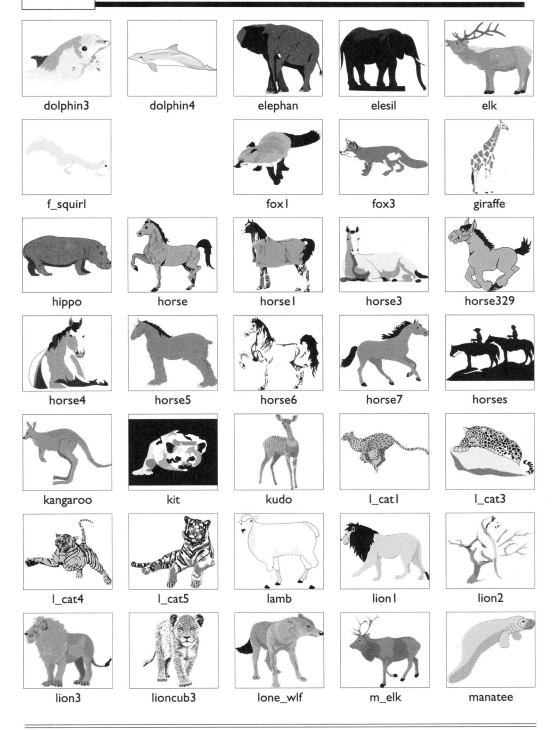

dolphin3	dolphin4	elephan	elesil	elk
f_squirl		fox1	fox3	giraffe
hippo	horse	horse1	horse3	horse329
horse4	horse5	horse6	horse7	horses
kangaroo	kit	kudo	l_cat1	l_cat3
l_cat4	l_cat5	lamb	lion1	lion2
lion3	lioncub3	lone_wlf	m_elk	manatee

Animal
Animaux
Animales
Tiere

molegold

mongoose

monkey1

monkey2

mousec

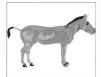

mule

otter

pig

platpus

prdog

pride3

rabbit1

rabbit2

rabbit3

rabbit4

rat

rcoon

rcoon2

rhino

rhino2

sealbaby

sealion

sheep

sheepmt

sloth

squirel2

squirrel

symb016

symb020

symb365

symb538

symb539

symb541

symb546

symb547

symb548

symb549

symb550

walrus

weasel

whale1

whale2

whale3

wolf1

wolf2

zebra1

zebra2

blakcat

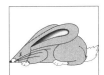
bunny

dog_a

dog_b

dog_c

dog_d

goodmorn

Animal
Animaux
Animales
Tiere

afghan

antelopt

apricotm

armadilo

asianele

baboon

beagle

beart

beaver

begging

bitten

bloodhou

bobcat

boxkanga

buffalo

bullt

calf

caliccat

camel

camelf

caribou

caribou2

cat_dog

cat_win

cat_yarn

catfence

catnlimb

chihuahu

chipmunt

clydesda

collie

colt

commerso

common

cougar

cowhead

dalmatio

deer

doberman

dog_fite

dogfood

dogholdi

doghouse

dogpound

dogwfris

domseal

donkey

elepantt

elephntc

elkt

fawn

gazelle

giraffed

giraffes

goat

goatface

gorilla

greyhund

grizzlyb

guidedog

h_seal

hamster

hippofac

hippot

horselt

horseins

horsekic

horseonh

hospcat

hospdog

Animal
Animaux
Animales
Tiere

hrsehead

hyena

jumpkang

killwhal

kitten

koala

l_cougar

lambt

leopard

lion

llama

longhorn

lyingcam

mammoth

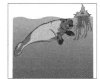
manateet

marmot

milkcow

milkgoat

mink

mole

monkeys

moose

mountain

opossum

oranga

ottert

oxcart

pac_dolf

panda

pcamel

pig_2

piglet

pigt

platypus

pointer

Animal
Animaux
Animales
Tiere

polarcub

porcupin

prairdog

puppy

puppywsl

rabbit

raccoon

ram

redfox

reindeer

rhinot

roarlion

rockhou

roo

runaway

saltydog

scottish

seal

shar_pei

sheept

siamese

skunk

slamb

sleepdog

sow

spotted

squirret

sttiger

tabbycat

tail

taswolf

tiger

tortoise

toypoodl

walrust

Animal
Animaux
Animales
Tiere

warthog

wbuffalo

whippet

wolf

yak

zebrat

Arrow
Fléches
Flecha
Pfeile

arrow01

arrow02

arrow03

arrow04

arrow05

arrow06

arrow07

arrow08

arrow09

arrow1

arrow10

arrow11

arrow12

arrow13

arrow14

arrow15

arrow16

arrow17

arrow18

arrow19

Arrow
Fléches
Flecha
Pfeile

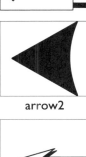
arrow2

arrow20

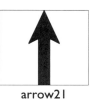
arrow21

arrow22

arrow23

arrow24

arrow25

arrow26

arrow27

arrow28

arrow29

arrow3

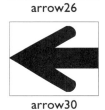
arrow30

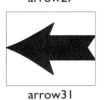
arrow31

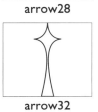
arrow32

arrow33

arrow4

arrow5

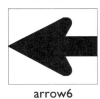
arrow6

arrow7

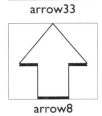
arrow8

arrow9

symb104

symb105

symb106

symb107

symb108

symb109

symb110

symb111

symb112

symb113

symb114

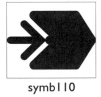
symb115

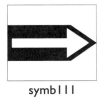
symb116

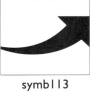
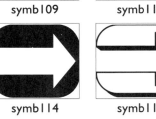
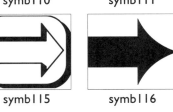

Arrow
Fléches
Flecha
Pfeile

symb117

symb118

symb119

symb120

symb121

symb122

symb123

symb124

symb371

symb385

symb386

symb590

symb591

symb592

symb593

symb594

symb597

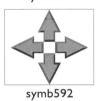
symb598

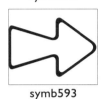
symb599

symb600c

symb601

symb602

symb603

symb604

symb605

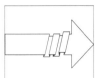
symb606

symb607

symb608

symb609

symb610

symb611

symb612

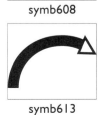
symb613

symb614

symb615

Arrow
Fléches
Flecha
Pfeile

| symb616 | symb617 | symb618 | symb619 | symb620 |

Arrows
Flèches
Flechas
Pfeile

  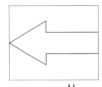 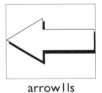

| arrow1d | arrow1ds | arrow1l | arrow1ls | arrow1o |

| arrow1r | arrow1rs | arrow1u | arrow1us | arrow2d |

    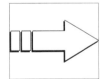

| arrow2o | arrow2u | arrow3o | arrow40 | arrow4o |

 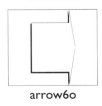 

| arrow5o | arrow6a | arrow6o | arrow7o | arrow8o |

Bird
Oiseaux
Pajaro
Vögel

2cranes

bdge_hnd

bird_tit

birdc

birdgrey

bljay

chick

chick2

chicken

cranec

crow

duckbab

duckc

eagle1

eagle2

emuc

falcan

farmhen

feather

goose

goosecsw

hawkc

hen

nestegg

newloon

ostrich

owl1

owl2

owl3

parrot1

parrot2

parrot3

pelican

61

Bird
Oiseaux
Pajaro
Vögel

pelican1

pelican2

pelican3

penfam

penguin1

penguin2

puffins

rooster1

rooster2

sponbill

sunbird

swan

symb021

symb052

symb213

symb543

symb544

symb545

tocan

vulture

Bird
Oiseaux
Pajaro
Vögel

birdi

dove

owl

parrot

parroti

turkeyi

Bird
Oiseaux
Pajaro
Vögel

eagle1o

eagle2o

eagle4

scream

us_eagle

Bird
Oiseaux
Pajaro
Vögel

allens	apelican	atlantic	bantam	barbet
barnowl	belted	bkcplory	black_br	bluebird
bluejay	bnest	bobwhite	brownboo	brownpel
bunting	canadago	canary	cardinal	chickent
chickt	chukar	cockfite	coftrock	condor
cranet	crowned	crowt	eaglefac	eaglehea
eagleper	earlybrd	egret	emperor	falcon

Bird
Oiseaux
Pajaro
Vögel

femaleal	finch	flamingo	flicker	flycatch

flyeagl1	flyeagl2	g_heron	gamehen	gentoo

gooset	greatowl	grebe	grosbeak	grouse

guinea	gulls	hatchegg	hornbill	kingfish

kingpeng	loon	lovebird	m_booby	macaw

magfriga	mallard	mandarin	nuthatch	oregonju

oriole	ostricht	parakeet	parrott	partrig

Bird
Oiseaux
Pajaro
Vögel

peacedov

peacock1

peacock2

pelicant

penguinc

penguins

petrel

pheasant

pigeon

pilings

quail

red_head

red_wing

rockhopp

rooster

roosterh

rosela

rosering

runner

s_goose

saw_owl

sbluewrn

scarleti

snowyowl

sparrow

spoonbil

spotted3

sunbirdt

swallow

swant

tanager

toucan

towhee

turkeyt

violett

Bird
Oiseaux
Pajaro
Vögel

vulturet

whistle

wilsons

woodduck

woodpeck

Business
Affaires
Negocios
Büro

Business Equipment
Equiment Bureau
Equipo Negocias
Büro-Ausstattung

barcode1

boxlite

brefcas

brifcasa

calc

calcu01

cash1

cash2

cashierc

chair1

chair2

cliphold

clipp

copier

copier1

copier2

copier3

desk1

desk2

desk3

desk4

desk5

draftab

fax1

fax2

Business
Affaires
Negocios
Büro

Business Equipment
Equiment Bureau
Equipo Negocias
Büro-Ausstattung

fax3

fax4

filecab

labeller

overhead

pager

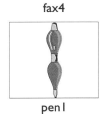

pen1

pen2

pencilc

pens

rapicom1

sharpner

stapler1

symb06

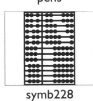

symb228

symb351

symb378

symb427

symb519

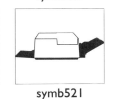

symb521

symb522

tacks

tape

taxes

telindex

thmbtack

accident

busalien

deathtax

file_cab

flybrief

henchman

hungry

hypnotiz

in_dangr

mac_user

mnitrhed

pen

phoneyou

phonfeud

photcopr

postbomb

scanner

snails

taxesi

time_fly

trading

walkcase

whlbrrw

workholc

workload

wrongvid

Business
Affaires
Negocios
Büro

Business Equipment
Equiment Bureau
Equipo Negocias
Büro-Ausstattung

adding

box

brief

callbell

fax

file

fountain

holder

pencil

pocket

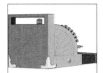

register

cardfile

stapler

ticker

type

wallt

waste

Celebration
Célébration
Festivo
Feier

anniv048

baloons

bang049

boom051

cork030

crack032

cupid033

cupid034

fwork052

gift021

Celebration
Célébration
Festivo
Feier

hat066

nyear029

party387

symb288

toast281

Celebration
Célébration
Festivo
Feier

annivers

bdaycake

bdaycaki

bdayegg

bdaygift

bells

c_tail

c_tail3

celebrat

celebrtn

champag

chamspla

cupidi

ferwhel

gradcap

grads

happynyr

introduc

invited

jmarried

Celebration
Célébration
Festivo
Feier

partyhat

rockets

storki

stovehat

wedring

Celebration
Célébration
Festivo
Feier

anniver2

bang_

cake

champagn

cinco

cornucop

dragont

fathers

firecrak

firework

mardi_l

mardi_2

pow_

rocketst

stork

toasting

Child
Enfants
Niño
Kinder

babyi

bikestnt

boy_ball

boydog

boyplayg

brandnew

brat

bubgumkd

chldblox

chldbook

chldcoco

chldplay

chldstdy

chldswng

chldtddy

girl_dog

girl_toy

harpi

kid

kids

kidsplay

kidwball

makeface

poplick

praying

skatbord

skatbrd

skatbrdj

teaparty

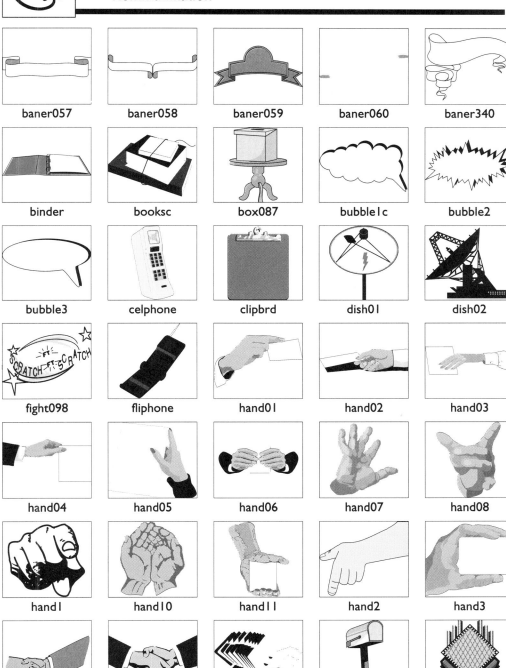

baner057	baner058	baner059	baner060	baner340
binder	booksc	box087	bubble1c	bubble2
bubble3	celphone	clipbrd	dish01	dish02
fight098	fliphone	hand01	hand02	hand03
hand04	hand05	hand06	hand07	hand08
hand1	hand10	hand11	hand2	hand3
handshkb	handshkc	index	mail086	marqe357

Communication
Communication
Comunicación
Kommunikation

marqe358	mick343	micro01	micro02	modem1
modem2	modem3	openbook	phone01	phone02
phone03	phone04	phone05	phone06	phone07
phone08	phone09	phone10	phonec	shakec
swirl095	symb011	symb032	symb033	symb036
symb042	symb070	symb071	symb072	symb073
symb074	symb075	symb076	symb077	symb078

Communication
Communication
Comunicación
Kommunikation

symb079

symb080

symb081

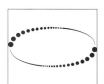
symb082

symb085

symb086

symb087

symb088

symb089

symb090

symb160

symb161

symb162

symb163

symb208

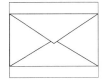
symb210

symb229

symb379

symb380

symb404

symb469

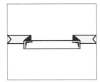
symb487

symb491

symb523

symb524

symb530

symb536

symb621

symb622

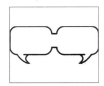
symb623

symb624

symb625

symb626

tele081

wind097

announce

artistim

badconct

book

book_a

booksi

bubblgal

bubblguy

goodidea

handsha

involved

micropho

phonrng1

phonrng2

phonsell

phonshwr

radio

reminder

satelite

scroll

sug_box

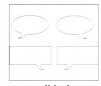
talkbub

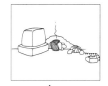
tech_sup

thotbubl

typesetr

yahoo

banner1

banner2

banner3

banner4

comunica

hand_out

handshk1

handshke

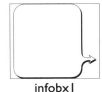
infobx1

infobx2

infobx3

infobx4

mailbox

milsat

radaro2

Communication
Communication
Comunicación
Kommunikation

antique

british2

dial

hand

mailboxt

okt

pointing

satdish

shaking

stamp

thumb

touch

Computer
Ordinateur
Ordenadores-computadora
Computer

3d2key

3d3key

3dkey

antwchip

cdhand

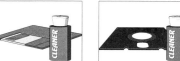
cleaner1

cleaner2

click

cmpunit3

compr082

compu01

compu02

compu03

compu04

compu05

compu06

compu07

compu08

compu09

compu10

compu11

compu12

compu13

compu14

compu15

compu16

conbox

datatape

discase

disk

disk3a

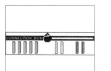
disk3b

disk5a

dsdrive1

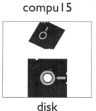
dsdrive2

Computer
Ordinateur
Ordenadores-computadora
Computer

duplic1

duplic2

flopdr01

flopdr02

flopdr03

flopdr04

flopdr05

flopdr06

game01

game02

hand09

hdrive1

hdrive2

hdrive3

ibmm

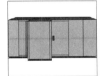
ibmproc1

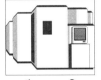
ibmproc2

ibmt

iccard01

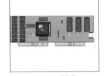
iccard02

input

joystick

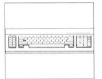
kboard1

kboard2

kboard3

kboard4

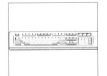
kboard5

kboard6

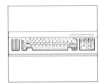
keytext1

keytext2

kmc01

kmc02

kmc03

kmc04

kmc05

kmc06

kmc07

kmc08

kmc09

kmc10

kmc11

kmc12

kmc13

kmc14

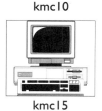
kmc15

kmc16

kmc17

kmc18

kmc19

kmc20

kmc21

kmc22

kmc23

kmc24

kmcbw01

kmcbw02

kmcbw03

kmcbw04

laptop01

laptop02

laptop03

laser01

laser02

laser03

laser04

laser05

laser06

laser07

laser08

laser09

Computer
Ordinateur
Ordenadores-computadora
Computer

laser10

linotron

mac01

mac02

mackey

matrix1

matrix2

matrix3

matrix4

montor01

montor02

montor03

montor04

montor05

montor06

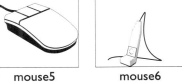

montor07

montor08

montor09

montor10

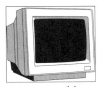

montor11

montor12

mouse1

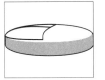

mouse2

mouse3

mouse4

mouse5

mouse6

networkc

optdisk1

optdisk2

output

pcfax

phsyco

pickupc

ploter01

Computer
Ordinateur
Ordenadores-computadora
Computer

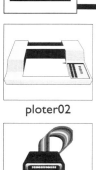

ploter02

ploter03

plug01

plug02

plug03

plug04

plug05

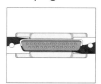

plug06

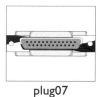

plug07

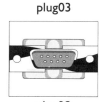

plug08

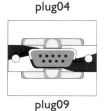

plug09

plug10

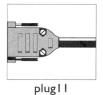

plug11

pocket1

port3

printer

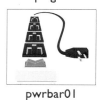

pwrbar01

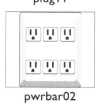

pwrbar02

qboard

scanner1

scanner2

scanner3

stylus

symb045

symb164

symb165

symb166

symb167

symb168

symb179

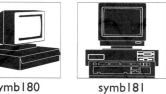

symb180

symb181

symb182

symb183

symb184

Computer
Ordinateur
Ordenadores-computadora
Computer

symb185

symb186

symb187

symb362

symb363

symb517

symb518

symb520

texas01

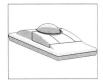
trakball

Computer
Ordinateur
Ordenadores-computadora
Communication

bud_mail

bus_mac

compwiz

disks

emergncy

glad_mac

lifehold

lovlttrs

macntosh

mad_mac

srpr_mac

virusi

3480c

cptterm

desktop3

dp_2655

grid

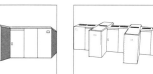

ibm3090

ibm30906

ibm3180

ibm3380

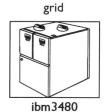

ibm3480

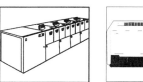

ibm3480s

ibm4224

ibm4381

ibm_at

ibm_pc

ibm_tape

ibmps2

lino300

linorp2

lsrwr

maciifx

maciix

macse30

wiswkstn

wisws93

z_248

Computer
Ordinateur
Ordenadores-computadora
Computer

diskette

ibm

lino

macii

macse

next

talking

Crest
Ecusson
Cresta
Abzeichen

Air Force
Armeé de l'air
Fuerzous Aéras
Luftwaffe

adtebom

af_coa

afacad

afcom

afelec

afint

afit

aflogcm3

aflogcom

afrotc

afsyscom

aftrncm

airtrc2

airuniv

airweth

alaskcmd

alpa

alskcom

asd

comfed

Crest
Ecusson
Cresta
Abzeichen

Air Force
Armeé de l'air
Fuerzous Aéras
Luftwaffe

elescom

genmgrs

logcom

mac

maccom

macunshd

norad

oast

pac

romeadc

rsrvecom

sac

sac l

sacshd

sdic

seccom

seslog

seslogn

spacecom

spacmd

syscom

tac

tac2

taccom

tracom

usaf l

usaf2

usafnews

usafrcsv

Crest
Ecusson
Cresta
Abzeichen

Army
Armée
Militar
Armee

100divs1

100divt1

101abdc

101airb1

102infd1

102infs1

104divs1

104dvsl1

104dvsr1

104dvtr1

106divs1

108div1

108divs1

10armcs1

10armys1

10infds1

11airds1

11armcs1

11armrd0

11thaird

12armcs1

13airds1

13armcs1

13thsup

14armcs1

15armcr1

15armys1

16armcs1

17airds1

18aircr1

18aircs1

18thair

197infbr

19armcr1

1infdvs1

Crest
Ecusson
Cresta
Abzeichen

Army
Armée
Militar
Armee

| 1stcav | 1usarms1 | 1usarmy1 | 20armcs1 | 21corp1 |

| 22armcs1 | 23armcs1 | 23armds1 | 23armrd0 | 23armyc1 |

| 24armcr1 | 24armcs1 | 24thmech | 25infds1 | 25infdv1 |

| 26infds1 | 26infdv1 | 28infds1 | 28infdv1 | 2armcor1 |

| 2calvs1 | 2infdiv1 | 2infdvs1 | 2ndarmor | 2usarms1 |

| 35infds1 | 35infsl1 | 35infsr1 | 36armyc1 | 38infds1 |

| 38infdv1 | 3corps1 | 3infdiv1 | 3infdvs1 | 3rdarmor |

Crest
Ecusson
Cresta
Abzeichen

Army
Armée
Militar
Armee

3rdaryhq

3rdcorp

3usarms l

40infds l

40infdv l

42infds l

42infdv l

47infnt0

47infny0

49armr

4ardivs l

4armycr l

4infdiv l

4infdvs l

4usarms l

4usarmy l

50armor

5armdiv l

5corp

5corpsl l

5infdiv l

5infdvs l

5usarms l

5usarmy l

63infys l

65infys l

66infys l

69infys l

6armcrs l

6infdiv l

6usarms l

6usarmy l

70_divs l

70divtr l

7 l infys l

Crest
Ecusson
Cresta
Abzeichen

Army
Armée
Militar
Armee

75infdv l	75infty0	76_divn	76_divs l	77infds l

77infdv l	78div l	78divs l	79infds l	79infdv l

7armcrs l	7infdiv l	7usarms l	80divsl l	80divtr l

8 l infdv l	82airdv l	82ndair	83infds l	83infdv l

84div l	84divsl l	85divsl l	85divtr l	86infds l

87infds l	88infds l	89div l	89divsl l	8armcrs l
8infdiv l	8tharmy l	8usarms l	8usarmy l	90infds l

Crest
Ecusson
Cresta
Abzeichen

Army
Armée
Militar
Armee

one mile up inc

91divsll | 91divtrl | 92infdsl | 92infdvl | 93infdsl

94infdvl | 95divl | 96infdsl | 97infdsl | 98dvtrsl

99infdsl | 9armcrl | 9armcrsl | 9corpl | 9infdivl

9infdvsl | 9usarmsl | aeuruc | armcorsl | armresrv

armstaff | armsthi | armyeur | armyntlg | armyseal

armystfl | arsenal | arsenall | centcom | chapasst

chapast | cib | cicmduc | civilaf | civilaff

Crest
Ecusson
Cresta
Abzeichen

Army
Armée
Militar
Armee

comcmd

criminv

criminvl

crincoml

darpa

darpablk

dca

devices

dia

dla

dma

dma_aero

dma_dstr

dma_schl

dmahydro

dna

dna_worm

dod_av

dod_finc

dod_ig

dodaudit

dodbicen

dsshield

dsstorm

engbiuc

eoa_ce

eoa_hc

eoa_int

eoa_is

eoa_mc

eoa_mddc

eoa_t

essayons

famlysup

fmf_pacl

Crest
Ecusson
Cresta
Abzeichen

Army
Armée
Militar
Armee

fregurd1

frscmu

gen_stf1

genstaff

haec_prt

health1

infocom

infocom1

inspgen

intlcom

intlcom1

intlgnc

intlgnc1

jdgadvg

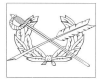

jdgadvgl

mil_dc

mili_dc

mterial

ntlgdbu

ntlgrdbu

ntlguard

pac_vctr

pacific

pacific1

pmguewd1

pmguvad1

qtr_mstr

qtrmstr

s_opercm

secr_arm

serving

soceur

swordfr1

swrdfree

transcom

Crest
Ecusson
Cresta
Abzeichen

Army
Armée
Militar
Armee

transcor

transp

trdocuc

trdocucc

usarmy1

usforco1

voice

war_clge

warantof

wescom

westcom1

Crest
Ecusson
Cresta
Abzeichen

Navy
Marine
Marina
Marine

achnavop

aegis

aircom

armsout1

armsouth

auditser

bmedsurg

chfnavop

china_lk

civileng

cnet

comatlnc

comeurp

compac

comsea

Crest
Ecusson
Cresta
Abzeichen

Navy
Marine
Marina
Marine

cpo1

cvhelo

dchnavop

lamps

macsea

nardac

nav_rsrv

navacdmy

navair

navaircm

navdac

naveltcm

navfaccm

navfuel

navintcm

navinvsr

navocean

navperm

navpub

navrvsrf

navsea

navseal1

navsecgp

navspacm

navsup

navtelcm

navwarcg

navy

navy90

navychap

navyemb

navyrgfn

navyshdw

noarl1

nosc

Crest
Ecusson
Cresta
Abzeichen

Navy
Marine
Marina
Marine

nosc_re1

nrl_logo

nrlnew

nswc

nusc1

nvypubpr

pac_com1

ptmugun1

sealftc1

sews1

spawar

subgru9

uscg

uscg_200

uscgseal

usmc

usmc1

usmcatv

usnwoman

warrant

Crest
Ecusson
Cresta
Abzeichen

Other
Autre
Otras
Andere

aarc

afghanis

afgharc

alar

angar

angola

antar

arabsl

argentin

ausar

Crest
Ecusson
Cresta
Abzeichen

Other
Autre
Otras
Andere

austrli

bar

bavarc

bbyarc

bdar

bdsar

belgium

bgar

bgarc

bharc

bhutar

bjar

bolar

brar

brazil

brnar

bruarc

bsar

bulgaria

burkar

buruar

camear

canada

car

cdnar

cdnarc

chadar

chile

china

ciar

coar

columbia

comoar

crarc

csar

Crest
Ecusson
Cresta
Abzeichen

Other
Autre
Otras
Andere

cuba

cverarc

cyar

czech

dar

denmark

djiar

dkar

domar

domrar

dyar

dzar

eakar

ecarc

egunarc

egypt

esarc

estar

etar

etarc

ethar

euro_cm

far

fbyarc

fjiarc

flar

france

gabar

gbuisar

gcaarc

germany

ghar

grar

great_br

greece

Crest
Ecusson
Cresta
Abzeichen

Other
Autre
Otras
Andere

guinar

guyar

har

heidarc

hngary

hondar

humaneso

ilar

inda

indar

indoar

iragar

iran

iranar

iraq

ireland

irlar

isar

isl

israel

italy

jaar

japan

job_corp

jorar

jordan

kampuchi

kar

kinbarc

kuwait

kwtar

laoar

lar

latar

lebanon

Crest
Ecusson
Cresta
Abzeichen

Other
Autre
Otras
Andere

lesar

libar

libyaar

lithar

maar

malaysl

maldsl

malisl

maltar

marshsl

mexarc

mexico

microsl

monsl

mozar

msar

mwsl

myanar

namar

nato

nepasl

netherla

ngrasl

nicarc

nigeria

nigersl

nkorar

nlsl

northye

norway

nsl

nzsl

omanar

pakistan

paksl

Crest
Ecusson
Cresta
Abzeichen

Other
Autre
Otras
Andere

panama

pansl

papngar

pchinar

pear

pearc

peru

phillipi

philsl

plarc

qatar

raar

rbar

rcaar

rcbar

rchar

rchnarc

respond

rharc

rimsl

rlarc

rmar

roar

rokar

rparc

russia

russia2

s_africa

safrsl

saudiara

senesl

sfar

southye

spain

spainsl

Crest
Ecusson
Cresta
Abzeichen

Other
Autre
Otras
Andere

srilsl

stlucar

stomar

stvinsl

sudansl

surinar

swazsl

swedar

sweden

switzerl

syria

syrsl

taiwan

tanzar

tbirdlog

thailand

thaisl

togoar

trinsl

tunisar

tunisia

turkey

turksl

uarabsl

uganda

ugansl

ukrflsl

uksl

un

unisrvad

unitedae

uragsl

vanatar

venezuel

venzar

Crest
Ecusson
Cresta
Abzeichen

Other
Autre
Otras
Andere

venzarc

vietar

vietnam

warranto

wgar

wjar

wsamar

yemenar

yugoar

yugoslav

zairear

zambsl

zimbar

Crest
Ecusson
Cresta
Abzeichen

United States
États-Unis
Estados-Unidos
USA

aid1

aid2

annuit

apl

brprison

bu_altbf

bu_engpr

cia

congrss

custm_tr

dc_seal

dea

dot_shld

dpt_agr

dpt_agr1

Crest
Ecusson
Cresta
Abzeichen

United States
États-Unis
Estados-Unidos
USA

dpt_com

dpt_def

dpt_def1

dpt_edc

dpt_edu1

dpt_enr

dpt_hhs

dpt_hhs1

dpt_hud

dpt_int

dpt_jst

dpt_lbr

dpt_nvy

dpt_nvy1

dpt_st1

dpt_st2

dpt_tra

dpt_trs

dpt_trs1

dpt_vet

dpt_vet1

eeo

eeoc1

epa

faa

faa1

faa_whi

fcc

fdic

fedlwscl

fema

fema1

fema_eg

ferc

Crest
Ecusson
Cresta
Abzeichen

United States
États-Unis
Estados-Unidos
USA

fishwild

ftc

gao

gao l

gpo

gsa

gsa l

health

houseo

irs_tres

jpl_arw

landmgmt

ncua

niddk

nih

noaa

nrc l

nsa

omb

omb_pres

park_srv

peacecor

pres

pres02

resrv_bd

rtrstcom

sba_logo

sba_seal

senate

serving

spacerib

thrft_sv

tva

us_army

us_mint

Crest
Ecusson
Cresta
Abzeichen

us_schld

usa

usaclear

usgs

usps1

usps2

viseal

Crustacean
Crustacés
Crustáceo
Krustentiere

COREL

clams

crab

goodmusl

lobster1

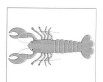

lobster2

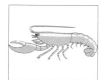

lobster3

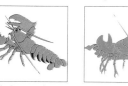

lobster4

lobster5

shell1

shell2

snail

anemone

barnacle

bubble

cabrits

chiton

cone

dungenes

flameaug

hawk_win

helmet

hermit

limpet

lobster

miter

nautilus

redabalb

redabalt

sandoll

shellt

snailt

spiney

starfsh1

starfsh2

starfsh3

sweetlip

tentoliv

triton

turrid

vex

yoka

Design
Esquisse
Deseñio
Design

back1

back3

burst

gridc

icon001

icon002

icon003

icon004

icon005

icon006

icon007

icon008

icon009

icon010

icon011

icon012

icon013

icon014

icon015

icon016

icon017

icon018

icon019

icon020

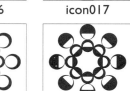

icon021

icon022

icon023

icon024

icon025

icon026

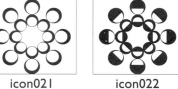

icon027

icon028

icon029

icon030

icon031

icon032

icon034

icon035

icon036

icon037

icon038

icon039

icon040

icon041

icon042

icon043

icon044

icon045

icon046

icon047

icon048

icon049

icon050

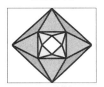
icon051

icon052

icon053

icon054

icon055

icon056

icon057

icon058

icon059

icon060

icon061

icon062

icon063

icon064

icon065

icon066

Design
Esquisse
Deseñio
Design

icon067

icon068

icon069

icon070

icon071

icon072

perspect

star

star2c

symb043

symb495

symb551

symb552

symb553

symb554

symb555

symb559

symb560

symb561

zing050

boycameo

bttrfly

bushel

draftin

floral10

floral11

floral12

floral13

floral14

floral15

floral_1

floral_2

floral_3

floral_4

floral_5

floral_6

floral_7

floral_8

floral_9

florali1

florali2

florali3

florali4

florali5

florali6

floursh1

floursh2

floursh3

floursh4

fruit

fruittre

hearts1

leaf

leaf_wr

maski

Design
Esquisse
Deseñio
Design

minstrel

nouv_a

nouv_b

nouv_c

nouv_d

nouv_e

nouv_f

nouv_g

nouv_h

nouv_i

nouv_j

nouv_k

nouv_l

nouv_m

nouv_n

nouv_o

nouv_p

nouv_q

nouv_r

nouv_s

nouv_t

nouv_u

nouv_v

nouv_w

nouv_x

nouv_y

nouv_z

seashell

snake_fl

chip01

chip02

chip03

colorbar

flow01

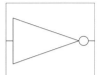

flow02

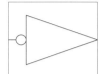

flow03

flow04

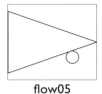

flow05

flow06

flow07

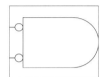

flow08

flow09

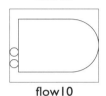

flow10

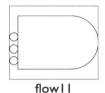

flow11

flow12

flow13

flow14

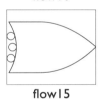

flow15

flow16

flow17

flow18

flow19

flow20

logiprob

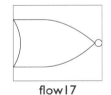

loop

microchp

multmetr

scope

semi01

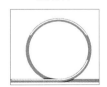

semi02

semi03

semi04

semi05

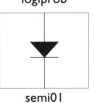

semi06

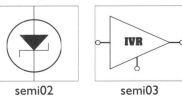

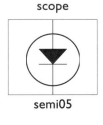

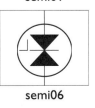

Electronic
Electronique
Electronica
Elektronik

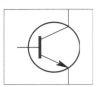

semi07

semi08

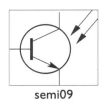

semi09

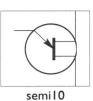

semi10

semi11

semi12

semi13

semi14

semi15

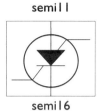

semi16

semi17

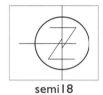

semi18

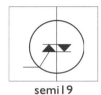

semi19

semi20

silwafer

switch01

switch02

symb211

symb222

symb488

symb537

tablet

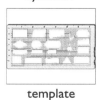

template

trans1

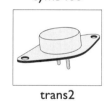

trans2

trans3

Fantasy
Imaginaire
Fantasia
Phantasie

l amazon

l angel

l bones

l centaur

l dragon

l elf

l tigl

l unicorn

l viking

l warrior

l wings

bopeep2

centr330

dumpty2

mychaul

nh1_2

peter2

pinnoch2

rapuns2

red2

scrooge2

skull042

snow2

th2_2

th3_2

th4_2

th5_2

winghors

Fantasy
Imaginaire
Fantasia
Phantasie

TOTEM GRAPHICS

cinderel

dragon

godmom

kingnept

mermaid1

mermaid2

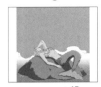

mermaid3

robotic

sserpent

Fire
Feu
Fuego
Feuer

COREL

fireman

firex

pumper

s13

s14

s15

s16

s18

sign175

sign176

sign177

sign178

sign179

sign180

sign181

sign182

sign183

sign184

sign185

sign186

Fire
Feu
Fuego
Feuer

sign187

sign188

sign189

symb170

Fire
Feu
Fuego
Feuer

alarm

bedfr

escap

ext1

ext2

ext3

extus

feel

firea

fireb

firec

firef

firem

firet

fladr

fpump

frsym

hatax

house

hzrds

plugs

roll

siren

anchovy

bluefin

fish

fishscor

jumpfish

octopus1

octopus2

octopus3

perchwh

perchyel

salfish1

salfish2

seahorse

shark1

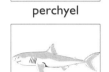
shark2

shark3

shark4

squid

stingray

symb370

symb540

symb542

tropcal

Fish
Poisson
Pescado
Fisch

anchovt

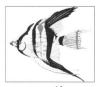
angelfis

arawana

atlanti

b_shark

Fish
Poisson
Pescado
Fisch

balloonf

banded

barb

barracud

bluegill

brtrout

burmeist

carp

catfish

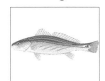
channelb

char

chum

clownfis

coelacan

cometgol

darter

discus

doradot

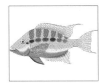
fire

flounder

flyfish

gar

glasseye

grayling

grouper

grtwhite

guppie

halibut

hamshark

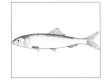
herring

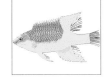
hogfish

laktrout

leafy

lesserel

lgbass

lionfish

loach

longnose

mano_war

marlin

moorishi

moray

nassau

notho

octopus

opah

oscart

padfish

perch

pickerel

pigmysun

pike

piranha

pollock

porkfish

pumpknse

qtrigger

queenang

rainbowt

redsnap

regal

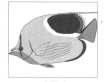
saddleba

sailfin

seabass

seahorst

siamesef

skipjack

smbass

sockeye

sole

Fish
Poisson
Pescado
Fisch

spsqfish

squidt

squrfish

starryfl

stop

stribass

striped

stripedp

sturgeon

swordtel

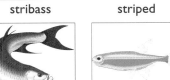

tarpon

tetra

texasska

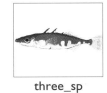

three_sp

trigger

truecod

trunk

walleye

whalesh

Flag
Drapeaux
Bandera
Flagge

austral

belgium3

british

canada3

french

germany3

swede

switz

Flag
Drapeaux
Bandera
Flagge

Africa
Afrique
África
Afrika

  COREL

ORGANIZATION of AFRICAN UNITY

afriorg

ALGERIA

algeria

ANGOLA

angolac

BENIN

benin

BOPHUTHATSWANA

bophutha

BOTSWANA

botswana

BURKINA FASO (UPPER VOLTA)

burkinaf

BURUNDI

burundi

CAMEROUN

cameroon

CAPE VERDE

capeverd

CENTRAL AFRICAN REPUBLIC

centafri

CHAD

chad

CISKEI

ciskei

CONGO

congo

DJIBOUTI

djibouti

EYGPT

egyptc

EQUATORIAL GUINEA

eqtguine

ETHIOPIA

ethiopia

GABON

gabon

THE GAMBIA

gambia

GHANA

ghana

GUINEA-BISSAU

guineabi

GUINEA

guineac

IVORY COAST

ivorycoa

KENYA

kenya

LESOTHO

lesotho

LIBERIA

liberia

LIBYA

libya

MALAGASY REPUBLIC (MADAGASCAR)

malagasy

MALAWI

malawi

MALI

mali

MAURITANIA

mauritan

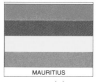

MAURITIUS

mauritiu

MOROCCO

morocco

MOZAMBIQUE

mozambiq

Flag
Drapeaux
Bandera
Flagge

Africa
Afrique
África
Afrika

 COREL

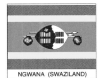

NGWANA (SWAZILAND)

ngwana

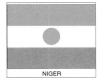

NIGER

niger

NIGERIA

nigeriac

OLD CAMEROUN

oldcamer

OLD DAHOMEY

olddahom

OLD EYGPT

oldegypt

OLD ETHIOPIA

oldethio

OLD LIBYA

oldlibya

RWANDA

rwanda

SÃO TOMÉ-PRINCIPE

saotomep

SENEGAL

senegal

SIERRA LEONE

sierrale

SOMALIA

somalia

SOUTH AFRICA

sthafric

ST HELENA

sthelena

SUDAN

sudan

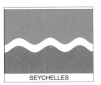

SEYCHELLES

sychelle

TANZANIA

tanzania

TOGO

togo

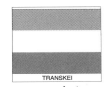

TRANSKEI

transkei

TUNISIA

tunisiac

UGANDA

ugandac

ZAIRE

zaire

ZAMBIA

zambia

ZIMBABWE

zimbabwe

Flag
Drapeaux
Bandera
Flagge

Asia
Asie
Asia
Asien

AFGHANISTAN

afganist

AZAD KASHMIR

azadkash

BANGLADESH

banlades

BHUTAN

bhutan

BURMA

burma

CHINA (PEOPLES REPUBLIC)

chinac

COMORO ISLANDS

comorois

HONG KONG

hongkong

INDIA

indiac

INDONESIA

indonesi

JAPAN

japanc

KAMPUCHEA

kampuche

KIRIBATI

kiribati

REPUBLIC OF KOREA

korea

KOREAN PEOPLE'S DEMOCRATIC REPUBLIC

kpd

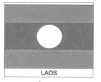

LAOS

laos

MALAYSIA

malaysia

MALDIVE ISLANDS

maldivei

MONGOLIA (PEOPLE'S REPUBLIC)

mongolia

NEPAL

nepal

VIETNAM (NORTH)

nvietnam

OLD AFGHANISTAN

oldafgan

OLD LAOS

oldlaos

OLD VIETNAM (SOUTH)

oldvietn

PAKISTAN

pakstan

SINGAPORE

singapor

SRI LANKA

srilanka

TAIWAN

taiwanc

THAILAND

thailan

TONGA

tonga

TURKEY

turkeyc

125

Flag
Drapeaux
Bandera
Flagge

Canada
Canada
Canada
Kanada

ALBERTA

alberta

BRITISH COLUMBIA

britcolm

CANADA

canadac

flag040

MANITOBA

manitoba

NEW BRUNSWICK

newbruns

NEWFOUNDLAND

newfound

NOVA SCOTIA

novascot

NORTH WEST TERRITORIES

nwt

ONTARIO

ontario

PRINCE EDWARD ISLAND

pei

QUEBEC

quebecc

SASKATCHEWAN

saskatch

YUKON

yukon

Flag
Drapeaux
Bandera
Flagge

Central America
Amérique Centrale
Centroamérica
Mittleamerika

ANGUILLA

anguilla

ANTIGUA AND BARBUDA

ant_bar

BAHAMAS

bahamas

BARBADOS

barbados

BELIZE

belize

BERMUDA

bermuda

BRITISH VIRGIN ISLANDS

bvisland

CAYMAN ISLANDS

caymanis

COSTA RICA

costaric

CUBA

cubac

CURAÇAO

curacao

DOMINICA

dominica

DOMINICAN REPUBLIC

domnrep

EL SALVADOR

elsalvad

GRENADA

grenada

Flag
Drapeaux
Bandera
Flagge

Central America
Amérique Centrale
Centroamérica
Mittleamerika

GUATEMALA

guatemal

HAITI

haiti

HONDURAS

honduras

JAMAICA

jamaica

MEXICO

mexicoc

MONTSERRAT

montserr

NETHERLANDS ANTILLES

nethant

NICARAGUA

nicaragu

PANAMA

pnama

PUERTO RICO

puertori

SAINT LUCIA

sntlucia

ST. KITTS-NEVIS

stkittne

SAINT VINCENT
and the GRENADINES

stvincen

TRINIDAD AND TOBAGO

trinidad

TURKS AND CAICOS ISLANDS

turkscai

Flag
Drapeaux
Bandera
Flagge

Europe
Europe
Europa
Europa

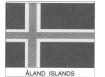

ÅLAND ISLANDS

alandisl

ALBANIA

albania

ALDERNEY

alderney

ANDORRA

andorra

AUSTRIA

austria

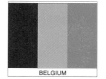

BELGIUM

belgiumc

BULGARIA

blgaria

BOSNIA-HERZEGOVINA

bosniahe

EUROPEAN COUNCIL

cncleurp

CROATIA

croatia

Flag
Drapeaux
Bandera
Flagge

CZECHOSLOVAKIA

czechozl

DENMARK

denmarkc

ENGLAND: CROSS of ST GEORGE

england

FAROE ISLANDS

faroeisl

FINLAND

finland

FRANCE

francec

GERMAN DEMOCRATIC REPUBLIC

gdr

GERMANY (WEST)

germanyc

GREECE

greecec

GREENLAND

greenlan

GUERNSEY

guernsey

HUNGARY

hungaryc

ICELAND

iceland

IRELAND

irelandc

ISLE of MAN

isleofmn

ITALY

italyc

LIECHTENSTEIN

liechten

LUXEMBOURG

luxembou

MACEDONIA

macedoni

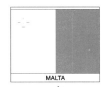

MALTA

malta

MONACO

monaco

MONTENEGRO and SERBIA

monteneg

NETHERLANDS

nethrlan

NORTHERN IRELAND

nireland

NORWAY

norwayc

OLD AUSTRIA

oldaustr

POLAND

poland

PORTUGAL

portugal

ROMANIA

romania

SAN MARINO

sanmarin

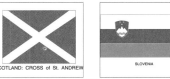

SCOTLAND: CROSS of St. ANDREW

scotland

SLOVENIA

slovenia

SPAIN

spainc

SWEDEN

swedenc

SWITZERLAND

switerla

Flag
Drapeaux
Bandera
Flagge

Europe
Europe
Europa
Europa

 COREL

UNITED KINGDOM

uk

UNION OF SOVIET
SOCIALIST REPUBLICS

ussr

VATICAN CITY STATE

vaticanc

WALES

wales

YUGOSLAVIA

yugosla

Flag
Drapeaux
Bandera
Flagge

Middle East
Moyen-Orient
Medioeste
Naher Osten

 COREL

BAHREIN

bahrein

CYPRUS

cyprus

IRAN

iranc

IRAQ

iraqc

ISRAEL

israelc

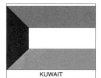

JORDAN

jordanc

KUWAIT

kuwaitc

LEBANON

lebanonc

OLD IRAN

oldiran

OLD SYRIA

oldsyria

OMAN

oman

QATAR

qatarc

SYRIA

syriac

UNITED ARAB EMIRATES

uae

YEMEN
(ARAB REPUBLIC)

yemenarc

YEMEN
(DEMOCRATIC PEOPLES REPUBLIC)

yemenpd

Flag
Drapeaux
Bandera
Flagge

Other
Autre
Otras
Andere

BRITISH ANTARCTIC TERRITORY

batc

BUDDIST FLAG

buddhist

COMMONWEALTH SECRETARIAT

comnwlth

FEDERATION INTERNATIONALE
des ASSOCIATIONS VEXILLOLOGIQUES

fedvexil

flag

HERM

herm

NORTH ATLANTIC
TREATY ORGANIZATION

natoc

piratec

FLAG of the RACE

race

UNITED NATIONS

unc

AIR FORCE

usairfrc

Flag
Drapeaux
Bandera
Flagge

Pacific
Pacifique
Pacífico
Pazifik

AMERICAN SAMOA

amrsamoa

AUSTRALIA

austrlia

BRUNEI

brunei

COOK ISLANDS

cookisla

FIJI

fiji

FRENCH POLYNESIA

frchpoly

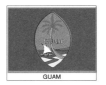

GUAM

guam

MARSHALL ISLANDS

marshall

MICRONESIA

micrones

NAURU

nauru

NEW ZEALAND

newzeala

NIUE

niue

NORTH MARIANAS ISLANDS

nmariana

OLD BURMA

oldburma

PALAU

palau

Flag
Drapeaux
Bandera
Flagge

Pacific
Pacifique
Pacífico
Pazifik

PAPUA NEW GUINEA

papuanew

PHILIPPINES

philippi

SOLOMON ISLANDS

solomani

TUVALU

tuvalu

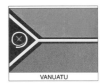

VANUATU

vanuatu

VENDA

venda

WESTERN SAMOA

westsamo

Flag
Drapeaux
Bandera
Flagge

South America
Amérique Latine
Sudamérica
Südamerika

ARGENTINA

argntina

ARUBA

aruba

BOLIVIA

bolivia

BONAIRE

bonaire

BRAZIL

brazilc

CHILE

chilec

COLOMBIA

clumbia

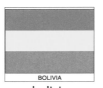

ECUADOR

ecuador

FALKLAND ISLANDS

falkland

GUYANA

guyana

OLD BOLIVIA

oldboliv

PERU

peruc

PARAGUAY (OBVERSE)

pgobvers

PARAGUAY (REVERSE)

pgrevrse

SURINAM

surinamc

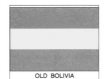

URUGUAY

uruguay

VENEZUALA

venezue

Flag
**Drapeaux
Bandera
Flagge**

United States
États-Unis
Estados-Unidos
USA

alabama

alaska

arizonac

arkansas

batlflag

benningt

bonniebl

californ

coastgrd

colorado

confed1

confed2

confed3

confed4

connecti

delaware

dstofcol

flag037

florida

georgia

grndunio

hawaii

idaho

illinois

indiana

iowa

kansas

kentucky

louisian

maine

maryland

massachu

michigan

minnesot

mississi

Flag
Drapeaux
Bandera
Flagge

United States
États-Unis
Estados-Unidos
USA

MISSOURI

missouri

MONTANA

montana

NEBRASKA

nebraska

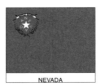

NEVADA

nevada

NEW ENGLAND

newengla

NEW HAMPSHIRE

newhamps

NEW JERSEY

newjerse

NEW MEXICO

newmexic

NEW YORK

newyork

NORTH DAKOTA

northdak

NORTH CAROLINA

nrthcaro

NATIONAL FLAG
1775 - 1800

ntnl1775

NATIONAL FLAG
JUNE 1777 - APRIL 1795

ntnl1777

NATIONAL FLAG
JULY 1818 - SEPT. 1818

ntnl1818

NATIONAL FLAG
JUNE 1777 - APRIL 1795

ntnlflag

OHIO

ohio

OKLAHOMA

oklahoma

OREGON

oregon

PRESIDENT

presiden

PRESIDENT

presiden

RHODE ISLAND

rhodeisl

SECRETARY of NAVY

scnavyus

SOUTH CAROLINA

southcar

SOUTH DAKOTA

southdak

TENNESSEE

tennesse

TEXAS

texas

UNITED STATES OF AMERICA

usac

VIRGIN ISLANDS of the USA

usavi

UTAH

utah

VERMONT

vermont

VIRGINIA

virgnia

VICE PRESIDENT

vpusa

WASHINGTON

washingt

WEST VIRGINIA

westvirg

WISCONSIN
1848

wisconsi

Flag
Drapeaux
Bandera
Flagge

United States
États-Unis
Estados-Unidos
USA

wyoming

Flag
Drapeaux
Bandera
Flagge

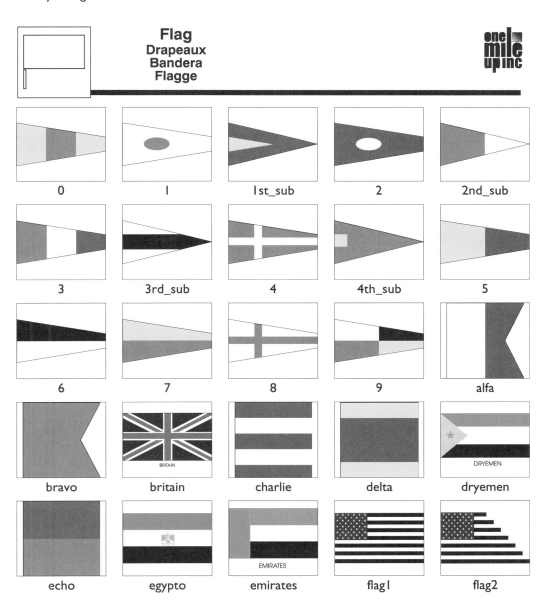

0	1	1st_sub	2	2nd_sub
3	3rd_sub	4	4th_sub	5
6	7	8	9	alfa
bravo	britain	charlie	delta	dryemen
echo	egypto	emirates	flag1	flag2

134

flag6nat

foxtrot

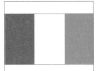
franceo

golf

hotel

india

irano

iraqo

israelo

jordano

juliett

kilo

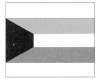
kuwaito

lima

mike

novembr

oscar

papa

quebec

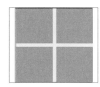
romeo

saudiarb

secnav

sierra

syriao

tango

turkeyo

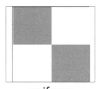
uniform

us_flag

usflag

usflag_p

victor

whiskeyo

xrayo

yankeeo

yemen

Food
Alimenation
Comida
Lebensmittel

Drinks
Breuvage
Bebidas
Getränke

beer

beer070

can

coffee

draft

drinka

milk

minwater

orangej

symb039

symb040

symb369

symb444

symb445

symb499

winebotl

Food
Alimenation
Comida
Lebensmittel

Fruit & Vegetable
Fruits et Légumes
Frutas y veg
Obst & Gemüse

almonds

apple

applea

apricot

artchoke

aspargus

aspgus

avacado

banana

beet

Food
Alimenation
Comida
Lebensmittel

Fruit & Vegetable
Fruits et Légumes
Frutas y veg
Obst & Gemüse

cabbage

canmelon

cantlope

cauliflr

celery

cherrie1

cherrie2

corn

cornicop

cucumber

cucumbra

eggplant

garlic

goodbean

goodberr

goodcarr

goodgrap

goodleek

goodlime

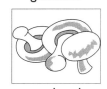
goodmush

goodpeac

goodpear

goodpepp

goodpump

goodspud

goodtom

goodtom1

grapes

kiwi

lemon

lemona

lettuce

mushrm1

mushrm2

olive

Food
Alimenation
Comida
Lebensmittel

Fruit & Vegetable
Fruits et Légumes
Frutas y veg
Obst & Gemüse

onion

orange

peachbsk

peanuts

peapod

radish

snopeas

squash

squash1

squash2

strawber

swpepper

symb447

symb448

symb449

symb450

symb455

symb456

symb457

wtrmelon

Food
Alimenation
Comida
Lebensmittel

Products
Produits
Productos
Molkereiprodukte

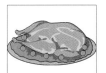

bird071

bowltoms

bread

brie

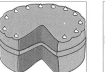

cake337

cheese

chescake

chese069

chilipep

Food
Alimenation
Comida
Lebensmittel

Products
Produits
Productos
Molkereiprodukte

chinese	chop	cofeebrk	donuts	eggmufin

eggs	enchilad	flourbag	fruitbwl	goodcake

goodcrio	goodleg	hamburg	hamburgd	hotdog

hotpeper	icecone	kabob	meat072	muffins

mustard	pancakes	peachpie	pie338	poundcak

pretzel	roast	salmon	shrimps	spagetti

	steak	sundae	surfturf	swissche

Food
Alimenation
Comida
Lebensmittel

Products
Produits
Productos
Molkereiprodukte

symb366

symb367

symb368

symb452

symb453

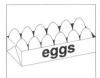

symb454

symb529

tenderln

tin074

tortelli

 Food
Alimenation
Comida
Lebensmittel

asparag

bakery

beeri

beermug

breakfas

cherries

cherry

cofeecup

coffeei

coktail

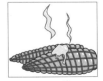

cornil

cornim

cornrost

croisant

dairyi

dinner

fortune

frank

frank2

franks

Food
Alimenation
Comida
Lebensmittel

Products
Produits
Productos
Molkereiprodukte

frnchfry

fruiti2

hambrg2

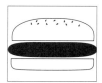
hambrger

icecream

lasagna

olivei

picnici

pie

pizza

pizzazz

popcorn

popcorni

rosturky

salad

seafood

shrimp

sodapop

spageti

sunday

sushi

sushi2

teacup

wheat

wine

Food
**Alimenation
Comida
Lebensmittel**

Drinks
Breuvage
Bebidas
Getränke

bottle

coffeet

hotcocoa

icddrink

martini

milkcart

sodapopt

whiskey

Food
**Alimenation
Comida
Lebensmittel**

Fruit & Vegetable
Fruits et Légumes
Frutas y veg
Obst & Gemüse

applet

artichok

aspargs

avocadoh

avocadow

bananat

beett

broccoli

cabbaget

cantalo

carrots

celeryt

corncob

cucumbrt

egplantt

garlict

grapest

kiwifrut

lemont

melon

Food
Alimenation
Comida
Lebensmittel

Fruit & Vegetable
Fruits et Légumes
Frutas y veg
Obst & Gemüse

 merry

mscene

 mushroom

 olimb

 olives

 onionhaf

 oranget

 osquash

 peach

 peanut

 peapods

 peart

 peas_pod

 pecans

 pineappl

 plum

 potato

 radisht

 raspberr

 sberries

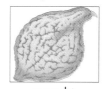 squasht

 tomato

Food
Alimenation
Comida
Lebensmittel

Products
Produits
Productos
Molkereiprodukte

applepie

bacon

biscuits

bowlsoup

breadt

candybar

catsup

ccookies

chescakt

choccake

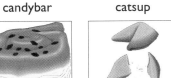
cinnroll

cookies

cpudding

ctnofegg

doughnut

fchicken

frbread

friedegg

fries

ham

hamburge

hotdogt

icecreat

lollypop

onionrin

pancaket

pizzasli

popcornt

popsicle

pretzelt

roasttur

salami

sandwich

sardines

sberrysh

144

nativity

nyear027

santa2c

santa3

santacat

sled007

sled022

sman019

stpat054

symb410

symb411

symb482

symb483

symb484

symb485

symb496

symb534

symb589

symbol3

witch044

witch045

witch046

xmas001

xmas002

xmas003

xmas004

xmas005

xmas006

xmas008

xmas009

xmas010

xmas013

xmas014

xmas015

Holiday
Festivités
Festivo
Feiertage

xmas016

xmas018

xmas023

xmas024

xmassky

xmaswish

Holiday
Festivités
Festivo
Feiertage

4thjuly

blitzen

candycan

chinyear

chris_wr

corncop

costume

eastbuny

easteggs

elf1

elf2

frosty

giftsi

hallween

hauntedi

huladanc

leprecan

manger

northpol

octfest

Holiday
Festivités
Festivo
Feiertage

parade

pumpkin

pumpkin2

reinder

santa

santacla

stardavd

stocking

stpabeer

stpagold

triktrea

us

xmas_hat

xmasbell

xmasgift

xmastree

yearsend

Holiday
Festivités
Festivo
Feiertage

angelt

bat

blackcat

bunny1

candycat

caroler

cupid

easterba

elf

franken

gifts	hallown2	hallown4	hangbat	hearts

holly	july4th	mangert	merrychr	mistltot

motherda	newyears	oldyear	ornament	pumpkin1

pumpkin3	pumpkn2t	rudolpht	santa2	santat
shepherd	skeleton	sleight	snowman	stockint
stpaddy1	stpaddy2	thanksg1	thanksg2	tourist

trailert	trick_or	tropical	valentin	valentnd

Holiday
Festivités
Festivo
Feiertage

veterans

weremask

witch

witcmask

wreath

xmasbelt

xmastret

Home
Domicile
Edificios
Zuhause

bear011

bookcase

bulb

can083

chair3

chair4

chest088

family

forsale

forsale1

iron

keys342

knife

lamp

lamp1

lamp2

lampa

light341

masktape

matches

openbox

pail

peppmill

qtipp

sctape

sissors

sltshake

smoke085

symb024

symb025

symb026

symb027

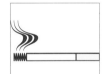

symb041

symb046

symb057

symb058

symb136

symb137

symb139

symb141

symb158

symb172

symb173

symb174

symb175

symb178

symb189

symb200

symb201

symb202

symb204

Home
Domicile
Edificios
Zuhause

symb205

symb206

symb207

symb232

symb250

symb256

symb396

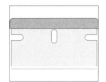
symb398

symb402

symb417

symb419

symb446

symb471

symb472

symb473

symb474

symb475

symb486

symb493

symb497

symb498

symb527

time068

toolbox

vack

vctorian

vcum084

wallc

zipper

Home
Domicile
Edificios
Zuhause

cigari

clock

clockout

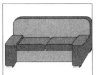
couch

forgeti

frighten

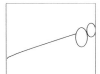
glassesi

litebulb

lock_key

mailboxi

moving

placeset

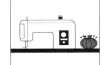
sewing

socketi

stool

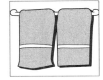
towels

utensils

Home
Domicile
Edificios
Zuhause

ashtray

butt

candlab

candle

flashlit

key

lampt

laundry

meter

pocket2

Home
Domicile
Edificios
Zuhause

salt_pep

scissors

swivel

tv

Insect
Insecte
Insecto
Insekten

ant

bee

beetle1

beetle2

bug285

bug286

bug287

bug288

bug289

bug328

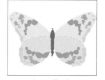

butfly1

butfly2

butfly3

buttrfly

centiped

dragflyc

flea

fly

fly1

fly2

grasshop

gribble

lice1

lice2

p_mantis

Insect
Insecte
Insecto
Insekten

spider1

spider2

squito

symb051

termite

web041

Insect
Insecte
Insecto
Insekten

americac

andrews

anthill

apollo

atlas

b_hlouse

barklous

bbeetle

blackwid

bluefly

bumblbee

califdog

caterpil

centipet

chafer

cicada

cleoptr

cloudedy

cockroac

cranefly

Insect
Insecte
Insecto
Insekten

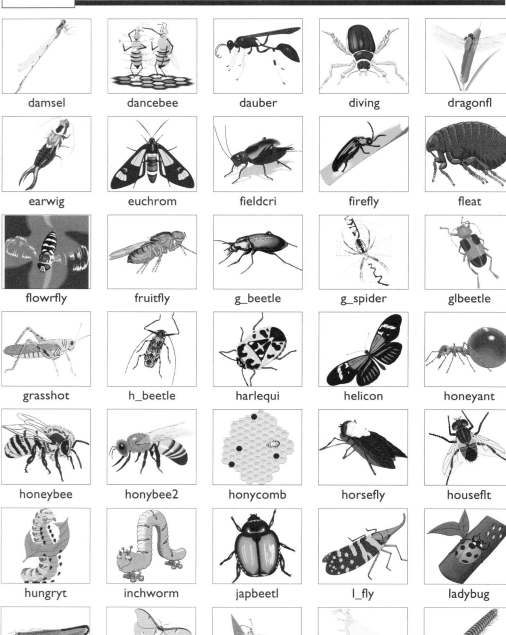

damsel	dancebee	dauber	diving	dragonfl
earwig	euchrom	fieldcri	firefly	fleat
flowrfly	fruitfly	g_beetle	g_spider	glbeetle
grasshot	h_beetle	harlequi	helicon	honeyant
honeybee	honybee2	honycomb	horsefly	houseflt
hungryt	inchworm	japbeetl	l_fly	ladybug
leafhopp	lunamoth	marbled	mayfly	milli

Insect
Insecte
Insecto
Insekten

monarchb

monarchc

monarcho

moonmoth

mosquitl

moths

nest

netwing

pasha

pbutter

prayingm

rainbowg

rbeetle

red_ant

sbeetle

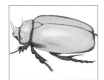
scarab

scorpion

silkworm

silver

softtick

sphinx

spiderc

stick

strider

summermo

swallowt

tbeetle

termitec

termitet

trant

velant

wasp

whiteadm

winged

yellowja

Insect
Insecte
Insecto
Insekten

z_butter

Insignia
Insignes
Insignias
Abzeichen

h1

h3

h4

plate01

plate02

plate03

plate04

plate05

plate06

plate07

plate08

plate09

plate10

plate11

plate12

plate13

plate14

plate15

plate16

plate17

plate18

plate19

plate20

plate21

plate22

Insignia
Insignes
Insignias
Abzeichen

plate23

plate24

plate25

plate26

plate27

plate28

plate29

plate30

plate31

plate32

plate33

plate34

plate35

plate36

plate37

plate38

plate39

plate40

plate41

plate42

plate43

plate44

plate45

plate46

plate47

plate48

plate49

plate50

plate51

plate52

plate53

plate54

plate55

plate56

plate57

plate58

plate59

plate60

plate61

plate62

plate63

plate64

plate65

plate66

plate67

plate68

plate69

plate70

plate71

plate72

plate73

plate74

plate75

plate76

plate77

plate78

plate79

plate80

Insignia
Insignes
Insignias
Abzeichen

one mile up inc

1lt

1sgtdev

1stscm

1stsmsgt

2lt

admiral

admiral1

air1stcl

air_def

airman

airstar

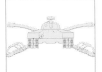

armor1

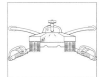

armor2

army01

armycrs1

aviatn

aviatn1

badge3

brig_gen

captain

captain1

captaino

castle_1

cavalry

chap_jew

chapchr1

chapchr2

chapjew

chemcor

chemcorp

chmsgt

cmndr

cmndr1

colonel

commofcr

comshore

corpeng

corpeng1

cpo

crowno

eagle3

eagle5

eaglptch

ensign

ensign1

eoa_tr

falconli

fc_mcpo

fieldar

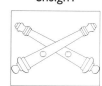

fieldart

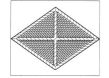

fin_corp

fincorp

forccom

forcom1

general

hiposeal

infntry1

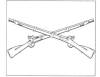

infntry2

jr_lt

jr_lt1

lieut

lieut1

ltcmndr

ltcmndr1

ltcol

ltgen

lwrradm

lwrradm1

major

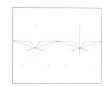

majorgen

mcpo

mcpon

mdcorvet

mdcorvt

medcorp1

medcorp2

meddentl

medspcl

medspcl1

medsrv1

medsrvcr

milintl

milintl1

milpoli

milpolic

mstrsgt

mudgupie

naveagle

navfltof

navwings

navywing

no_rank

nurscor

nurscor1

ordcorp1

ordcorp2

patchp01

patchp02

patchp03

rearadm

rearadm1

reseagle

scpo

seabee

sec_serv

sergeant

sgnlcor

sgnlcorp

shdstar

spclfor

spclforc

srairman

srmsgt

srwarshp

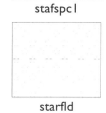

stafspcl

stafspec

star1o

star2o

star_5pt

starfld

stfsgt

submarin

supply

talons

tecsgt

torch

torch1

torch2

torch3

tradoc

tradoc1

trfmcom

trfmcom1

viceadm

viceadm1

wings1

wings2

wings3

wings4

wings5

wreath1

wreath2

z_amc_lo

z_rif_xp

z_x_pstl

Insignia
Insignes
Insignias
Abzeichen

caduceus

ems1

ems2

emt1

emt2

mdsym

patch

star1

star2

star3

Justice
Justice
Justicia
Justiz

con166

cop254

cop255

cop256

court

crook174

gunman

handcuff

jail292

judge207

judgec

mount171

mount172

mount173

scale1

scales

symb131

symb135

symb254

symb357

symb374

symb397

symb418

symb420

symb460

symb461

symb462

symb463

symb464

symb465

symb470

symb489

witness

Justice
Justice
Justicia
Justiz

burglari

detectiv

gangster

judge

judgei

policei l

policman

scalei

unifrcap

Justice
Justice
Justicia
Justiz

angryt

axe

burglar

chair

cop

drug

gavelt

judgec2

judgem

judget

lawyerl

mugger

noose

picpoc

prisoner

prost

sleeping

Landmarks
Monuments
Paisajes
Wahrzeichen

2morocco

arizona

bell056

chicago

chicago2

city

dallas

denver

eastr332

eiffle

japan2

losangel

mexico_2

newyorkc

poseidon

pyramid3

sanfran2

sanfranc

santorni

seattlec

symb005

symb006

symb007

symb059

vendmilo

venice

Landmarks
Monuments
Paisajes
Wahrzeichen

one mile up inc

capitolo

fedex

iwo_jima

jeff_mem

linc_mem

pentagon

shore_s

st_libty

supr_c

warcol

Landmarks
Monuments
Paisajes
Wahrzeichen

one mile up inc

wash_mon

white_hs

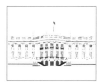

whitehss

Landmarks
Monuments
Paisajes
Wahrzeichen

TOTEM GRAPHICS

abbey

acrop

alamo

arch

australi

basils

bejing

bigben

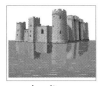

bodiam

canter

canyon

capitolt

catacomb

collos

country

disney

dogan

easteris

eiffel

empire

ggbridge

greatwal

hampton

indhall

libertyb

Landmarks
Monuments
Paisajes
Wahrzeichen

lincolnm

littlem

marines

mater

mesa

mykonas

niagara

oast

operah

pisa

puerto

pyramids

rio

rushmore

seattle

skyline

sphynx

statue

stone

tajmahal

torii

towerb

Leisure
Loisirs
Ocio
Freizeit

35mm

5678cue

admit356

b_alley

bino

cam

cards119

checker

chess349

dartclub

darts351

dice348

dream090

faces065

hand12

pool352

slot120

symb013

symb035

symb053

symb054

symb055

symb364

symb403

symb431

symb490

symbclub

symbdmnd

symbhart

symbspad

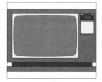

tele

vhs1

zoom

Leisure
Loisirs
Ocio
Freizeit

balet

camera

cards

dance

danceduo

dice

film

film l

filmi

maze

newspapr

photofrm

playcard

pony

projectr

suitcas

take_one

Leisure
Loisirs
Ocio
Freizeit

billiard

coaster

compact

desert

roulette

video

Man
Homme
Hombres
Mann

Business
Affaires
Negocios
Wirtschaft

abovdesk

bookman

boredman

bosfront

bossback

bosspose

bosswalk

bosswboo

bosswcas

bosswcof

busman

cartman

compman1

compman2

compman3

contruct

coverman

dashing

deskman2

deskman3

deskman4

dorwyman

draftman

executiv

feetup

files316

fixing

foreman

goldrush

humor140

humor141

humor142

humor143

humor144

humor153

Man
Homme
Hombres
Mann

Business
Affaires
Negocios
Wirtschaft

humor159

humor206

humor208

humor209

humor215

humor218

humor237

humor239

humor279

humor293

manchar

mandesk

manfront

manpose1

manpose2

manread

manreadn

manrush

mantalk

manwbook

manwcomp

manwibm

manwmac

manwpapr

manwphon

manwpile

measure

officman

onphone1

onphone2

overwork

phone196

phone198

phone199

phoneman

Man
Homme
Hombres
Mann

Business
Affaires
Negocios
Wirtschaft

read204

recline

relefman

reptech

signhere

speech

symb296

teleman

twofaced

type148

typeman

weldera

work212

work213

work214

work249

work250

work251

work252

work253

work258

work269

work270

work273

work274

work318

work320

worker1

worker2

workman3

Man
Homme
Hombres
Mann

Entertainment
Spectacles
Diversión
Underhaltung

actor110

actor111

actor113

choir324

clown036

clown1

curtnman

dirtr382

draw176

draw177

face114

host310

magic262

rock

rock263

rokstar

Man
Homme
Hombres
Mann

Historical
Histoire
Histórico
Geschichte

actor112

aristot1

beethov1

bethune1

brshnev1

cesarju1

columbs1

cromwll1

davinci1

edisont1

Man
Homme
Hombres
Mann

Historical
Histoire
Histórico
Geschichte

einst_a1

einstine

fordhn1

franklb1

genkhan1

grnt_ul1

gwash103

hanibal1

hemigwy1

henry8_1

hirohit1

howhugh1

htlerad1

ivanter1

kingtut1

krushev1

laurier1

lenin101

leninv1

lincn102

macavel1

mao_tt1

marxk1

mcdonal1

mking104

mlking1

mluther1

mozart1

npoleon1

nwtonis1

pearcew1

petegre1

poe_ea1

polom1

riel_lu1

Man
Homme
Hombres
Mann

Historical
Histoire
Histórico
Geschichte

robespr1

rooseve1

shakesp1

socrtes1

wshingt1

Man
Homme
Hombres
Mann

Humor
Humor
Humorismo
Humor

drink326

drunk267

drunk268

fman257

gone235

hop230

humor165

humor167

humor168

humor175

humor179

humor180

humor181

humor182

humor188

Man
Homme
Hombres
Mann

Humor
Humor
Humorismo
Humor

COREL

humor190

humor191

humor233

humor238

humor280

humor284

humor295

humor301

humor302

humor303

humor304

humor313

humor317

hunt327

lookn228

mad154

mail203

news202

ouch183

ouch234

paint178

phone309

point185

point300

shake187

shock294

sleep157

sleep243

sleep244

slide231

space321

time297

vtory192

yell236

Man
Homme
Hombres
Mann

Icon
Icône
Icono
Symbole

army379

chefc2

chefman

content

contrast

cooka

crouch

delivery

deskman1

dudeman

face118

facepose

graduatc

holmes

inchair

inspecto

kneeling

man1

man2

manback

paintin

poseman1

poseman2

poseman3

reading1

reading2

reading3

riding

running1

screamc

shruging

sitting1

snapshot

stetson

Man
Homme
Hombres
Mann

Icon
Icône
Icono
Symbole

symb018

symb019

symb125

symb126

symb127

symb128

symb129

symb130

symb132

symb133

symb134

symb263

symb267

symb268

symb269

symb270

symb272

symb275

symb282

symb283

symb284

symb285

symb286

symb287

symb294

symb305

symb306

symb308

symb421

symb422

symb423

symb424

symb428

symb440

symb441

Man
Homme
Hombres
Mann

Icon
Icône
Icono
Symbole

symb442

symb443

trolyman

victory

walking2

waveman

Man
Homme
Hombres
Mann

Miscellaneous
Divers
Varios
Verschiedenes

army100

artista

astronut

backwalk

bakeshop

binoculr

blueprin

bush_g

bxwface2

camraman

captainc

carry276

cave323

chefc1

cntrlman

cofee266

cookc

cookn277

cowboy1

cowboy2

Man
Homme
Hombres
Mann

Miscellaneous
Divers
Varios
Verschiedenes

docr259

doctr290

docwjar

doorman

draw169

eatn158

face106

face107

face108

face109

facesyd

grinder

hatman

heart035

help298

help299

hero170

hikerman

horseman

humor105

jman

knife325

knightgd

monfloor

moonwalk

oldman1

oldman2

paintera

paratrop

pilotc

pizzaman

profits

rancher

read145

read147

Man
Homme
Hombres
Mann

read149

read150

read200

read201

read205

readmag

relaxing

restn245

scentist

scrubdoc

seatman1

seatman2

seatman3

smoker

snow296

stndman1

stndman2

stndman3

stndman4

survey

taxi260

teacherc

thinkman

toocool

toxic

wait271

wait272

waiterc

walk222

walk224

walk312

walkrman

water247

waveflag

wizrd322

Man
Homme
Hombres
Mann

Miscellaneous
Divers
Varios
Verschiedenes

wow219

Man
Homme
Hombres
Mann

Sports
Sports
Desportes
Sport

b_baskp

basebat

basepich

batterc

bodybld1

bodybld2

bodybld3

boxer

cricket

exercycl

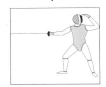

fencer

fishrma

footblla

ftbal131

ftbal132

ftbal133

ftbal134

ftbal135

ftbal136

ftbal138

ftbal139

ftbalrun

golf391

golfer

Man
Homme
Hombres
Mann

Sports
Sports
Desportes
Sport

gymrings

hockeyp

hocky389

horbug

horse2

jog220

jog223

jog226

jump229

jump232

jumper

man_ten

montclmb

oldjoger

pingpong

pitch394

pitcherc

pool137

poolplyr

run221

run227

run395

runnerc

skaboard

skate392

skate393

skier

skydiver

snow396

snowbord

soccr125

soccr126

soccr127

soccr128

soccr129

Man
Homme
Hombres
Mann

Sports
Sports
Desportes
Sport

soccr130

surfn248

waterski

Man
Homme
Hombres
Mann

Business
Affaires
Negocios
Wirtschaft

1040time

bizman

business

businman

busyboy

death

draftmai

foolery

forbes

grphbman

hon_bman

iaccocai

incentiv

jitters

meet_guy

memoi

paycustr

probsolu

proofing

quality

roster

s_jobs

salei

scullyi

speaker

Man
Homme
Hombres
Mann

stockdwn

stocksup

sucker

suit

trump

uptight

vip

Man
Homme
Hombres
Mann

arsenii

b_hope

big_g_k

clowni

cosbyi

d_rather

dj1

dj2

donking

e_murphy

eastwood

hrsn_frd

j_nchlsn

jagger

k_rchrds

l_nemoy

lettrman

rbn_wlms

rocknjon

rockstai

Man
Homme
Hombres
Mann

Entertainment
Spectacles
Diversión
Underhaltung

shwrzngr

singer

stallnei

w_crnkte

warnock

Man
Homme
Hombres
Mann

Historical
Histoire
Histórico
Geschichte

b_frnkln

beethovn

c_gable

chaplin

chrchill

confcius

custer

dali

einsteii

elvisi

fredastr

freud

g_khan

gandhi

george

grch_mrx

hemingwy

henry_8

hirohito

hitler

j_f_kndy

jn_wayne

Man
Homme
Hombres
Mann

Historical
Histoire
Histórico
Geschichte

khomeini

lincoln

m_l_king

marley

napoleon

picasso

s_dvs_jr

shakspre

socrates

w_c_flds

warhol

Man
Homme
Hombres
Mann

Humor
Humor
Humorismo
Humor

artistil

bar_code

blu_cllr

boss_off

briefi

burn_out

cheesy

clown

cold

cool

dancer2

daytimer

deadline

devil

distress

Man
Homme
Hombres
Mann

extchart

fax_faux

firstday

fly_man

generali

gimme

good_guy

goodytwo

guy

guypoint

guystrtc

happyguy

helipilo

hideseek

kickout

knockout

lawyer

legroom

listen

love_one

maili

mancouch

messengr

mon_morn

musleman

neandthl

nerd

nervousi

old_suck

outlaw

outlunch

paintri2

paste_up

pionerad

powernap

Man
Homme
Hombres
Mann

Humor
Humor
Humorismo
Humor

presentg

prisonr

program

real_out

red_tape

salesrat

seminar

shopping

sneaking

spaceman

special

stakwork

stikhell

stopi

stunned

surprguy

surprise

thnkguy1

thnkguy2

trainee

wake_up

washer

yelling

Man
Homme
Hombres
Mann

Icon
Icônes
Icono
Symbole

abe

artisti1

astrnaut

bnoculrs

bowing

Man
Homme
Hombres
Mann

businmi

butcher

cnstwork

coctail

danceri

hailcab

hiking

janitori

onstool

paintri l

phtgrphr

point

pointd

pointl

pointr

pointu

rockstar

shrug

sitting2

speaking

standing

trophy

winner

withcane

Man
Homme
Hombres
Mann

angel

angryi

arafat

awardman

barbeque

Man
Homme
Hombres
Mann

Miscellaneous
Divers
Varios
Verschiedenes

bartendr

bathtub

beginner

bird

bookworm

buddha

bush

butcher2

cashier

caveman

charles

chiseli

chretien

controlr

cook1

cooki

courier

cowboy

delivman

director

doctor

drilling

egypti

firemani

fuming

gb

gorbachv

grumpy

h_s_tmsn

hammeri

hunter

inspectr

khadafi

loungliz

mailman

Man
Homme
Hombres
Mann

Miscellaneous
Divers
Varios
Verschiedenes

male_sec

mandella

mandog

mitternd

monk

mowing

mulroney

musclei2

nervous

nixon

noriegai

north

painting

paintri3

peek

photogra

pirate

politicn

pope

prof

raincoat

readgoof

reagan

reagani

repairmi

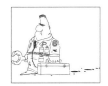
repairmn

retl_guy

runawayi

runscare

russiai

sawing

scientst

scrwdrv

servant

shave

Man
Homme
Hombres
Mann

Miscellaneous
Divers
Varios
Verschiedenes

shovelng

sitting

spaini

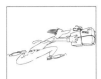
speedy

sumrtime

suntani

surgeon

talkguy

teachman

tiei2

trimmer

trudeau

typingi

waiteri

walensa

walking

wave_by

welder

welderi

whipman

wizard

worker

workman

zapped

Man
Homme
Hombres
Mann

Sports
Sports
Desportes
Sport

basebai2

basebali

baseball

bicycle

Man
Homme
Hombres
Mann

bowling

boxeri

footbai

footbal

footbali

golfi

golfplay

gretzkyi

hokyi

kareem

kungfu

mcenroe

nicklaus

run

runningi

ski

skieril

skierip

snobordi

surferi

tennisi

tyson

Man
Homme
Hombres
Mann

afoffcr

automati

c l7cp

enlisted

enlstblk

Man
Homme
Hombres
Mann

g_powell

genschw

gorbyo

helpil

husseino

kholmni

navyofcr

offcrblk

oficon

p_lincon

p_wshntn

pilot

pr_bush

pr_bush2

s_chaney

think1

think2

think3

think4

unc_sam

us_sldr

uscg_man

vp

vpquayle

weldm1

Man
Homme
Hombres
Mann

amanf

blindwlk

cold

docm

exerbike

lmanf

maledent

mdoctor

mouthgrd

nursm

ohead

orderly

param

patient

polm

sling

stretc

surgeon

Man
Homme
Hombres
Mann

Business
Affaires
Negocios
Wirtschaft

account

boss l

breakt

broker

burdened

cashiert

chinups

clip

contract

feet

inout

realtor

salesman

supers

taxi

Man
Homme
Hombres
Mann

Business
Affaires
Negocios
Wirtschaft

uptoass

Man
Homme
Hombres
Mann

Historical
Histoire
Histórico
Geschichte

abrahaml

columbus

georgewa

jesus

jesuscar

jesuscro

jouster

martin

samarai

Man
Homme
Hombres
Mann

Humor
Humor
Humorismo
Humor

| bedbug | beehive | boa | books | boss2 |

| buried | clownt | conan | crash | defeated |

| filling | garbage | graffiti | hacker | happyt |

| inter | janitor | lifting | mechanic | monkeyt |

| mulet | napping | siesta | sleep | sniff |

| spotted1 | tail2 | tguide | tip | traction |

worried

Man
Homme
Hombres
Mann

aborig

afdan

alaskan

alcohol

arab

baggage

bagpiper

bobby

calfropr

chef

chineseb

cigar

cuttert

drunkard

evzone

hearyea

hoisting

indian

israeli

jamaican

licking

mail

mending

mounty

news

palace

piratet

plowhrse

polit

reading

sailor

seacapta

snakec

split

spotted2

Man
Homme
Hombres
Mann

Miscellaneous
Divers
Varios
Verschiedenes

steerw

striker

suitt

taxid

tender

throne

tourpics

twogun

unclesam

vatican

waiter

yankee

yodel

Man
Homme
Hombres
Mann

Sports
Sports
Desportes
Sport

basketp2

basketpl

batter

bikerace

bowhunt

bowler

bronc

bullfite

bullridr

catcher

climber

diver

downhill

fencing

fin_line

202

Man
Homme
Hombres
Mann

Sports
Sports
Desportes
Sport

fisherma

ftballp2

ftballp3

ftballp4

ftballp5

ftballp6

ftballp7

ftballpl

gym_2

handweig

hockeyg

hockeypl

huntert

jetskier

ju_jitsu

karate

karate2

kendo

knocko

kungfut

longjump

madputte

pitcher

racehors

racehos2

referee

shaolin

shotput

skydivrt

snorkel

soccerp2

soccerpl

starting

sumo_I

sumo_2

Man
Homme
Hombres
Mann

Sports
Sports
Desportes
Sport

surfert

swimmer

waterskt

weightli

windsurf

Map
Cartographie
Mapa
Landkarte

Africa
Afrique
África
Afrika

CARTESIA

algeri_t

angola_t

benin_t

botswa_t

burkin_t

 (CAMEROON)

camero_t

(CENTRAL AFRICAN REPUBLIC)

ceafre_t

(CHAD)

chad_t

(CONGO)

congo_t

 *(DJIBOUTI)*

djibou_t

(EQUATORIAL GUINEA)

e_guin_t

(EGYPT)

egypt_t

(ETHIOPIA)

ethiop_t

 (GUINEA BISSAU)

g_biss_t

 *(GABON)*

gabon_t

 (GHANA)

ghana_t

 (GUINEA)

guinea_t

(IVORY COAST)

ivoryc_t

 *(KENYA)*

kenya_t

 (LESOTHO)

lesoth_t

 (LIBERIA)

liberi_t

 *(LIBYA)*

libya_t

 (MADAGASCAR)

madaga_t

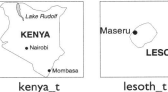 *(MALAWI)*

malawi_t

 (MALI)

mali_t

Map
Cartographie
Mapa
Landkarte

Africa
Afrique
África
Afrika

CARTESIA

maurit_t

morocc_t

mozamb_t

namibi_t

niger_t

nigeri_t

rwabur_t

s_leone

safric_t

saotom_t

senega_t

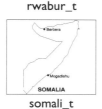
somali_t

sudan_t

swazil_t

tanzan_t

togo_t

tunisi_t

uganda_t

zaire_t

zambia_t

zimbab_t

Map
Cartographie
Mapa
Landkarte

Asia
Asie
Asia
Asien

CARTESIA

afghan_t

bangla_t

bhutan_t

brunei_t

china_t

Map
Cartographie
Mapa
Landkarte

Asia
Asie
Asia
Asien

india_t

indone_t

japan_t

kampuc_t

korea_t

laos_t

malays_t

mongol_t

myanma_t

nepal_t

pakist_t

papua_t

philip_t

srilan_t

taiwan_t

thaila_t

ussr_t

vietna_t

Map
Cartographie
Mapa
Landkarte

Central America
Amérique Centrale
Centroamérica
Mittleamerika

antill_t

bahama_t

belize_t

costari

cuba_t

domrep_t

elsalv_t

guatem_t

haiti_t

hondur_t

Map
Cartographie
Mapa
Landkarte

Central America
Amérique Centrale
Centroamérica
Mittleamerika

CARTESIA

jamaic_t

nicara_t

panama_t

prvi_t

trtob_t

Map
Cartographie
Mapa
Landkarte

Europe
Europe
Europa
Europa

CARTESIA
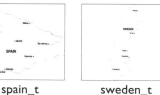

albani_t

austri_t

benelx_t

bulgar_t

czech_t

denmrk_t

finlnd_t

france_t

german_t

greece_t

hungry_t

icelnd_t

irelnd_t

italy_t

norway_t

poland_t

portug_t

romani_t

spain_t

sweden_t

switzl_t

ukire_t

yugosl_t

Map
Cartographie
Mapa
Landkarte

Middle East
Moyen-Orient
Medioeste
Naher Osten

bahrai_t

cyprus_t

iran_t

iraq_t

israel_t

jordan_t

kuwait_t

lebano_t

oman_t

qatar_t

saudia_t

syria_t

turkey_t

uae_t

yemen_t

Map
Cartographie
Mapa
Landkarte

North America
Amérique du Nord
Norte América
Nordamerika

canada_t

mexico_t

usa_t

Map
Cartographie
Mapa
Landkarte

Pacific
Pacifique
Pacífico
Pazifik

CARTESIA

austra_t

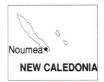

Noumea

NEW CALEDONIA

newcal_t

NEW ZEALAND

nz_t

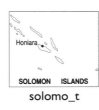

Honiara

SOLOMON ISLANDS

solomo_t

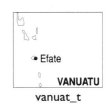

Efate

VANUATU

vanuat_t

Map
Cartographie
Mapa
Landkarte

CARTESIA

argent_t

BOLIVIA

La Paz
Cochabamba

Sucre

bolivi_t

BRAZIL

brazil_t

CHILE

chile_t

Barranquilla

Medellin
Bogota

Cali
COLOMBIA

colomb_t

Quito

Guayaquil

ECUADOR

equado_t

Cayenne

**FRENCH
GUIANA**

fr_guy_t

Georgetowr

GUYANA

guyana_t

PARAGUAY

Asuncion

paragu_t

Iquitos

Talara
PERU
Trujillo

Lima
Cusco

Arequipa

peru_t

Paramaribo

SURINAME

surinam

Salto

Montevideo

URUGUAY

urugua_t

Maracaibo
Caracas
Ciudad Guayana

VENEZUELA

venezu_t

Map
Cartographie
Mapa
Landkarte

Canada
Canada
Canada
Kanada

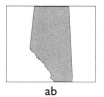

ab

bc

canada1

canada2

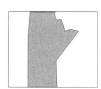

mb

nb

nfl

ns

nt

on

pe

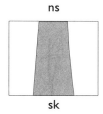

pq

sk

yt

Map
Cartographie
Mapa
Landkarte

Other
Autre
Otras
Andere

europec

mideast

n_amer_1

n_amer_2

slvnia

world1

world2

world3

Map
Cartographie
Mapa
Landkarte

United States
États-Unis
Estados-Unidos
USA

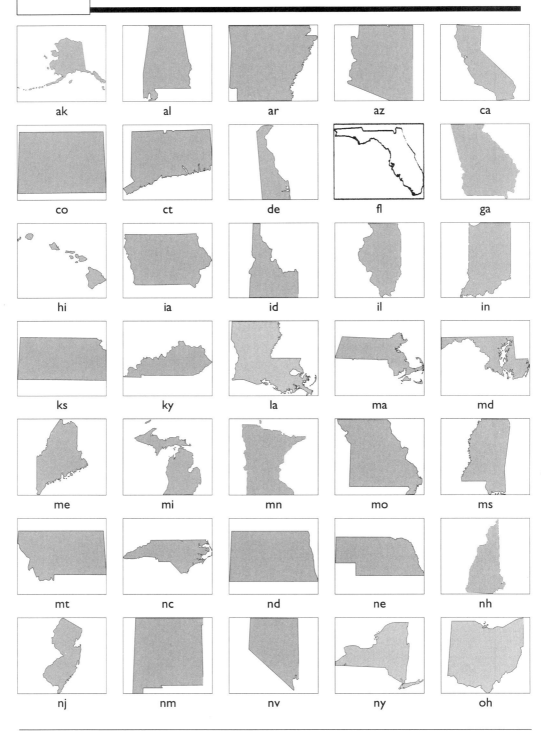

ak	al	ar	az	ca
co	ct	de	fl	ga
hi	ia	id	il	in
ks	ky	la	ma	md
me	mi	mn	mo	ms
mt	nc	nd	ne	nh
nj	nm	nv	ny	oh

Map
Cartographie
Mapa
Landkarte

United States
États-Unis
Estados-Unidos
USA

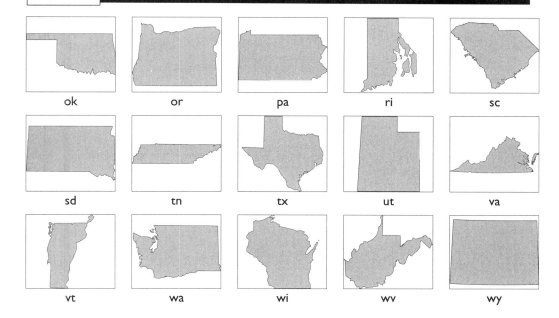

ok   or   pa   ri   sc

sd   tn   tx   ut   va

vt   wa   wi   wv   wy

Map
Cartographie
Mapa
Landkarte

Other
Autre
Otras
Andere

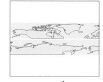

africa   arctprj   artcshr   asia   atlntshr

Map
Cartographie
Mapa
Landkarte

Other
Autre
Otras
Andere

europe

flatmap

globe

globeo

indnshr

latin_am

pacfcshr

reg_sym

slanted

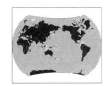

world

worldbl

Map
Cartographie
Mapa
Landkarte

United States
États-Unis
Estados-Unidos
USA

afbases

akmap

almap

armap

azmap

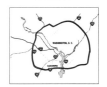

beltway

beltwmon

camap

comap

ctmap

demap

flmap

gamap

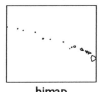

himap

iamap

Map
Cartographie
Mapa
Landkarte

United States
États-Unis
Estados-Unidos
USA

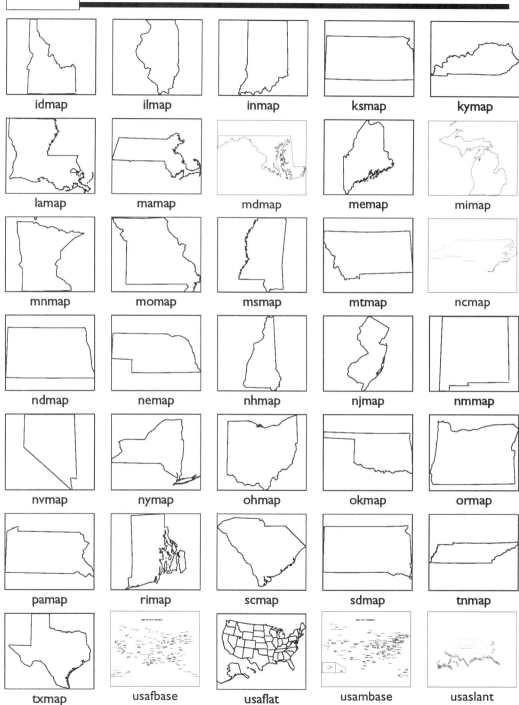

idmap	ilmap	inmap	ksmap	kymap
lamap	mamap	mdmap	memap	mimap
mnmap	momap	msmap	mtmap	ncmap
ndmap	nemap	nhmap	njmap	nmmap
nvmap	nymap	ohmap	okmap	ormap
pamap	rimap	scmap	sdmap	tnmap
txmap	usafbase	usaflat	usambase	usaslant

Map
Cartographie
Mapa
Landkarte

United States
États-Unis
Estados-Unidos
USA

usnabase

utmap

va_map

vamap

vtmap

wamap

wimap

wvmap

wymap

Medical
Médecine
Médico
Medizin

Anatomy
Anatomie
Anatomia
Anatomie

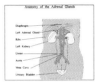

adrenal

alveoli

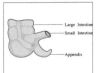

append22

appendix

appendiz

babyc

backmusc

bilepass

bladder

bloodcir

brain

brain2

brain3

breast

chest

circmion

coronary

digest

digestsy

diskslip

Medical
Médecine
Médico
Medizin

Anatomy
Anatomie
Anatomia
Anatomie

earc

earin

erect

eye

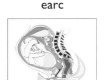

eyemuscl

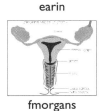

fetus

fmorgans

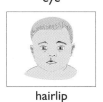

hairc

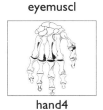

hairlip

hand4

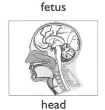

head

headmusc

heart

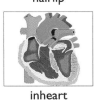

inheart

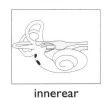

innerear

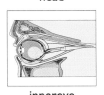

innereye

kidney

kneecart

labrinth

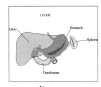

liverc

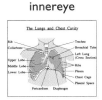

lungs

maletors

muscles

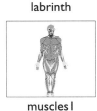

muscles1

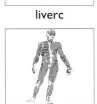

muscles2

nerves

nose

organs

pancreas

parathyr

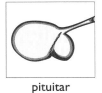

pituitar

profile

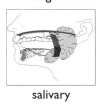

salivary

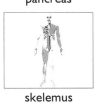

skelemus

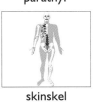

skinskel

Medical
Médecine
Médico
Medizin

Anatomy
Anatomie
Anatomia
Anatomie

skullc

smeltast

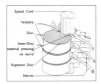

spine2

stomach

throatgl

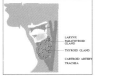

thyroid

torsofem

vagina

varicose

veins

Medical
Médecine
Médico
Medizin

Miscellaneous
Divers
Varios
Verschiedenes

symb029

symb030

symb227

symb257

symb258

symb297

symb298

symb299

symb300

symb301

symb302

symb303

symb304

symb309

Medical
Médecine
Médico
Medizin

Miscellaneous
Divers
Varios
Verschiedenes

symb310

symb314

symb358

symb425

symb426

symb566

wheelchr

Medical
Médecine
Médico
Medizin

Emergency
Urgence
Urgencia
Notfall

abthr

abuse

adblw

adlt1

adlt2

birth

blair

brth1

brth2

carry

cast

choke

cmrks

cpr1

cpr2

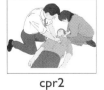

cpra

cprb

cprc

cprif

crawl

Medical
Médecine
Médico
Medizin

Emergency
Urgence
Urgencia
Notfall

crsh1

crsh2

crsh3

crvic

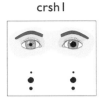
drown

eyeex

eyews

fallt

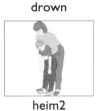
heim1

heim2

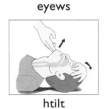
hopoi

htilt

ifblw

inf1

inf2

ipcac

knee

lead

mask

mast

pills

pool

pulcr

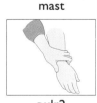
pulr1

pulr2

schild

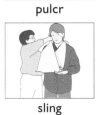
shock

sling

snake

splt1

splt2

stove

sweep

vicdn

water

219

Medical
Médecine
Médico
Medizin

Anatomy
Anatomie
Anatomia
Anatomie

aarm

aarme

aarmm

aboyf

achil

afem

afoot

afrep

ah&nm

ahand

ahipj

ahipm

ahips

aknej

aleg

alege

alegm

amale

amusc

ankl

anklejnt

aorta

apelv

aribs

arma

armt

armv

arter

arteries

artertot

askel

askul

aspin

atax

atax2

Medical
Médecine
Médico
Medizin

Anatomy
Anatomie
Anatomia
Anatomie

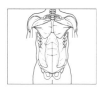

atorm

awrsj

baby

babywomb

bloodsup

bracp

breastt

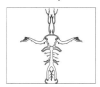

cwill

dfoot

diges

dorft

ear

earext

earext2

earint

elbowjt

embryo

endoc

eyeext

eyeint

facialn

faclmusc

femur

fert1

fert2

fert3

flkne

foot

frtskull

h&na

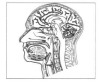

h&nek

h&nskel

h&nv

handt

headn1

Medical
Médecine
Médico
Medizin

Anatomy
Anatomie
Anatomia
Anatomie

headn3   headnek   hipjoint   humerus   icn03

icn10   icn11   icn12   icn13   icn16

kneejnt   lankj   larm   larme   larmm

latskull   lbrea   lchil   lega   legv

  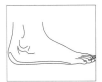

lelbj   lfem   lfoot   lh&nm   lhand

lleg   llege   llegm   lmale   lmusc

lskel   lskull   lspin   lymphsys   male

Medical
Médecine
Médico
Medizin

Anatomy
Anatomie
Anatomia
Anatomie

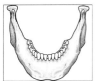

mandible

muscmas1

muscmas2

musman

nephr

nerve

nervessk

nervest

nervetot

oman1

otorso

parathy

parm

parme

parmm

pchil

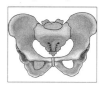

pelvis

pfem

pfoot

phand

phipm

pituitat

pknej

pleg

plege

plegm

pmale

pmusc

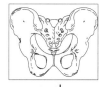

ppelv

prpts

pskel

pspin

ptorm

pwrsj

radulna

Medical
Médecine
Médico
Medizin

Anatomy
Anatomie
Anatomia
Anatomie

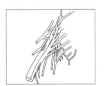

sacrp

shoulder

sinus

skeletn

skin

skin2

skullt

spine

spner

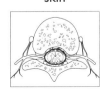

spsec

sssec

thoraxbo

tibfib

tmest

tmjcut

trach

trigemn

urin

veins

veinst

veinstot

venac

vert

vertebra

wristjnt

Medical
Médecine
Médico
Medizin

Dental
Dentaire
Odontologia
Zahneilkunde

aligflos

amlgburn

amlgcarr

badbrcs

beavflos

bonding

bonefile

braces

brshing1

brshing2

brshing3

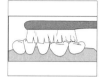
brshing4

bunyflos

canine

caninesc

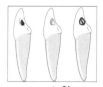
caninfil

cavprep

centoclu

chiptoth

chldexam

crown

curvscis

cutjaws

dds1

dds2

dds3

decdent

dent1

dent2

dentexam

dentflos

dmd1

dmd2

dmd3

drilbit

Medical
Médecine
Médico
Medizin

Dental
Dentaire
Odontologia
Zahneilkunde

drsplier

explorer

expprob

flospers

flossing

foodsbad

forceps

gumdis

handdril

hedgear1

hedgear2

hedgear3

hlthtoth

implants

incisor

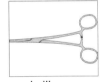

kellhemo

look1

look2

look3

manchair

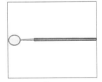

mirror

molar

molarfil

molarsc

mouthwsh

oclucav

ocluprof

oralcav1

oralcav2

ortho1

ortho2

permdent

persbrcs

persbrsh

premolar

Medical
Médecine
Médico
Medizin

Dental
Dentaire
Odontologia
Zahneilkunde

rootcanl

sabrbrsh

scaler

shrkbrsh

smile1

smile2

smile3

teeth

teethpro

teethviv

tethprof

tethvivo

teviv

tissuere

tothache

tothbrsh

tothfary

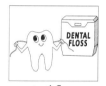

tothflos

tothjump

tothpste

walrbrsh

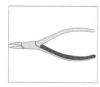

wirebend

wirecut

wisdteth

womchair

xrays

Medical Equipment
Equip Médical
Equipo Médico
Medizinisches Gerät

acebndag

autoclav

baid

bandaids

beaker

bldtest

board

bovie

bpcuf

bpcuff

cane

colar

crutches

dietscle

digtherm

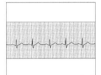

ekg1

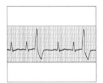

ekg2

ekg3

embox

eyechart

flask

glasses1

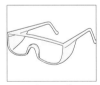

glasses2

glovet

hammer

hdblc

hdbnd

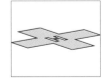

hpad

hsyringe

ivholder

jaws

jthrs

medalert

medtape

Medical
Médecine
Médico
Medizin

Medical Equipment
Equip Médical
Equipo Médico
Medizinisches Gerät

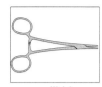

microscp   monit   mortpest   ndlehold   nedlhldr

o2tank   opscope   otoscope   pathsym   quadcane

resctor   scale   sharpsco   smask   steth

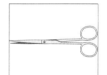

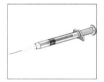

strscis   syringe1   syringe2   tdepress   therm

ultrasd   walker   whlchair

Medical
Médecine
Médico
Medizin

Organ
Organes
Órgano
Organ

adrenals

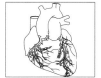

ahart

brainext

brainint

bronchi

digestiv

embry

estom

exeye

exhal

hact1

hact2

headn2

heartct

heartex

ibrai

icana

icn01

icn02

icn04

icn05

icn06

icn07

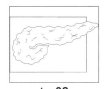

icn08

icn15

icn17

ihart

ineye

inhal

kidne

kidneyt

lbrai

lintc

liver

lungst

Medical
Médecine
Médico
Medizin

Organ
Organes
Órgano
Organ

ovaries

pancr

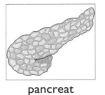

pancreat

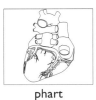

phart

reprof

reprom

resps

sbrai

sfrep

smrep

stomacht

stomc

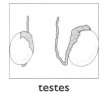

testes

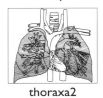

thoraxa2

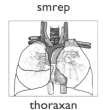

thoraxan

thyroidt

urinary

Miscellaneous
Divers
Varios
Verschiedenes

artist

award

brocol

carrots3

cheries

couple

cowboy3

dblbus

desk3g

drafting

grapes3

gymnast3

jazz3g

lips

magic3

marine3

movies

rhino3

shopbag

skier3

soccer3

tiger3

toucan3

vote

Miscellaneous
Divers
Varios
Verschiedenes

l cardeth

l lifelne

3beakers

anniv047

bordpass

broke336

compassc

cross06

cross13

cross18

cross7

fashion

frog

gear

glasses

globe339

gun089

heart061

heart335

jnbox067

m16rifle

pocwatch

rockt099

samander

sign1

sman020

symb056

symb171

symb188

symb392

symb492

symb494

symb525

watch

wood091

worldly

Miscellaneous
Divers
Varios
Verschiedenes

american

animals

atmblast

bbfrank

beard

beari

beeril

boot

bossbean

bug

bull

bushat

cannon

cap

cherylip

chopstik

cloud

cowbhat

creative

cruseshp

deskfeet

diamond

dragoni

drkcloud

elephani

fishi
 flagi
 flopyhat
 food
 gaspump

 gears
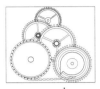 gearsi
 gearsout
 grimace
 holywood

 horsei
 housefly
 joker
 m_pencil
 martian

 medical
 microsco
 monkey
 muscle
 needle

 oilcan
 peterabt
 pipes
  rainclod
 safrihat

 shades
 shark
 slngshot
 smile
 snowflak

 snowmani
 stethscp
 sun
 talkmth
 tie

235

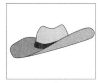

westhat

Miscellaneous
Divers
Varios
Verschiedenes

bookso

chain

claskids

cloudo

clouds

cocaine

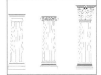

columns

crack

dollar

dolphin

electron

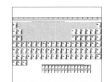

element2

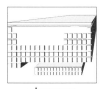

elements

femavia

frame1

frame2

gas_mask

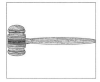

gavel

gavel_30

gear1

gear2

gearmsh

goato

heroin

ht_wires

hypo

lady_j

lgtcld

marijuan

mitvis

mulstar

radmain

rope

seahorso

sharko

shell

strtran

sunsrays

threemi

veterina

z_fram_3

Miscellaneous
Divers
Varios
Verschiedenes

amb1

amb2

blanket

breads

child

dairy

dog

fruits

hel1

hel2

hlthfood

meat

pcar

phone

saver

sayno

seat1

seat2

thumbs

afmask

armor

artnouvr

bible

budha

cannont

castle

cert7

chip

churcht

clownfic

constitu

diploma

eaglec

exec

fire2

flowerc1

flowerc2

flyfishc

frogo

 frogt

 fuse

 gasoline

 gauge

 goggles

 hotair

 hydro

 ibeam

 indianw1

 indianw2

 kicking

 magnify

 meter2

 mos_baby

 mosque

 mosquitc

 nuclear

 oilplat

 outline

 paperboy

 paperl

 passport

 prayer

 repub

 sailfish

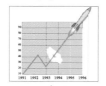 salest

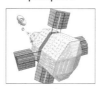 sat

 shoe

 snowflat

 stained

 steeple

 stop2

 stormy

 tadpole

 texesoil

Miscellaneous
Divers
Varios
Verschiedenes

torpedo

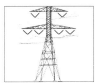
tower

treefrog

trophyt

tutmask

tweezers

watcht

well

windmill

Money
Monnaies
Dinerios
Geld

COREL

bagbroke

bagcash

bags

bank

bank076

bank080

bluenose

bundle

cartoon1

cartoon2

cartoon3

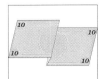
cartoon4

cartoon5

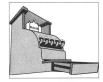
cash075

cash077

cash078

cash079

cash315

cashnozz

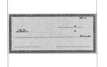
check

Money
Monnaies
Dinerios
Geld

check2

check3

compcash

finegold

handbuck

handcash

handcoin

handcysl

manwsafe

monybag

opencash

opensafe

passcash

pennyc

potogolo

prate

queene

sockcash

symb044

symb352

symb353

symb355

symb356

symb400

symb414

symb415

symb466

symb467

symb468

yen01

yen02

yen03

budget

flipcoin

galstrtc

money

money1

moneypit

mr_bill

potogold

sea_debt

stakcoin

timmoney

_golden

_green

bankt

bulbear

bullion

cash

copper

dime

grenade

moneyt

nickel

penny

Money
Monnaies
Dinerios
Geld

quarter

safe

scrooge

wallet

wealth

wheels

Music
Musique
Música
Musik

av01

av02

av03

av04

av05

av06

av07

av08

av09

av10

av11

cassette

clarinet

drum347

guitar

guitar05

harp345

horn017

music

piano344

Music
Musique
Música
Musik

pinoplr1	pinoplr2	play388	reels	saxophon
symb190	symb191	symb192	symb193	symb194
symb203	symb376	symb433	taps039	trombone
trumpet	violin	violn346	violnest	

Music
Musique
Música
Musik

cassetti

cd

cdi

keyboard

muscnote

musici

musician

musicim

musicnot

notepeop

panokyi2

piano

punk

sax

trumpeti

funkman

People
Gens
Gente
Leute

Business
Affaires
Negocios
Wirtschaft

2atdesk

2menwork

bordroom

comptwo1

comptwo2

convers2

convers3

convers4

edit

femshake

People
Gens
Gente
Leute

Business
Affaires
Negocias
Wirtschaft

fiveguys

groupof3

meeting

menshake

menwplan

sellcomp

threepeo

work319

workwalk

People
Gens
Gente
Leute

Icon
Icône
Icono
Sinnbild

convers1

couplea

crowd

dance031

dance2

forget

horsebak

office1

rafting

symb031

symb050

symb060

symb061

symb289

symb290

symb291

symb292

symb293

symb295

People
Gens
Gente
Leute

Icon
Icône
Icono
Sinnbild

 COREL

symb312

symb313

symb399

symb429

symb476

symb477

threepep

People
Gens
Gente
Leute

Miscellaneous
Divers
Varios
Verschiedenes

COREL

4_family

dad_kids

docsofis

doctexam

doctors

doctorsa

kiss386

kzooband

liftbabe

momnkids

onchlift

onpatio

parents

pose194

seattwo1

seattwo2

son_dad

stndtwo

twodance

twosuits

People
Gens
Gente
Leute

vaccine

vactn385

walktwo1

walktwo2

People
Gens
Gente
Leute

Business
Affaires
Negocios
Wirtschaft

b_meetin

headhunt

l_meetin

metingi

mornpapr

planning

saledown

salesup

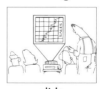

slide

wtrclrsh

People
Gens
Gente
Leute

Humor
Humor
Humorismo
Humor

boring

curious

customs

deadly

facade

family2

familyi

first_in

friendly

gonefish

hankpank

heapwork

kong

lrl_hrdy

nap_zap

network

phonecyc

picnic

piloti

stayawak

stfparty

stiknote

the_plan

triple

People
Gens
Gente
Leute

Icon
Icône
Icono
Sinnbild

businmen

chess

constrc

cple

cplehug

People
Gens
Gente
Leute

cpletalk

cplewltz

darts

fmlywalk

musicn

photgra

policei2

readbook

withbaby

People
Gens
Gente
Leute

Miscellaneous
Divers
Varios
Verschiedenes

beachcup

beatles

bedfllws

couplei

dating

finedin

fishrman

handshak

hockypls

lunch

parkcar

skilift

students

tennis

waitresi

wedngday

debrief

gen_mtg

maint

medevac

milconf

milind

molly

newunif

obs

probd

vj

People
Gens
Gente
Leute

aidsgrph

casting

doctor1

doctor2

doctor3

earexam

eyeexam

faces

icn09

injectn

medpeop

pediatrc

People
Gens
Gente
Leute

argue

arm

armwrest

home

hungary

judo

lovers

pat

physical

picnict

slaves

suntan

thechamp

weddingt

whisper1

whisper2

Plant
Botanique
Plantas
Pflanze

cactus

castiron

castor

cattails

deadtree

fern

flowiris

flwdaff

flwdaisy

flwr001	flwr1	flwr2	flwr3	laurelc
limb	massdrac	monstera	palm	phildron
plantc	sansever	scheffra	sentpalm	spiralfg
symb451	symb458	symb459	symb479	tree
tree093	tree1	tree2	tree3	tree4
tree5	treetop1	treetop2	treetop3	

Plants
Botanique
Plantas
Pflanzen

bonzai

boquet_I

boquet_2

cat_ll

cat_lr

cat_ul

cat_ur

cattail I

cattail2

flowers

tulips

Plants
Botanique
Plantas
Pflanzen

aarons

abutilon

allium

amarylis

anthur

aster

azalea

aztec

bachelor

bayleaf

beavrtlc

begonia

bellflow

bflower

bird_of

Plants
Botanique
Plantas
Pflanzen

blackeye	bleedngo	bloodroo	bluebonn	bottlebr
broadwil	camelia	capemari	carnatin	cherrybl
chinaros	chinesel	chives	chrysant	clantern
clover	columbin	crcactus	crocus	cyclamen
daffodil	dahlia	daisy	dandlion	dill
dogwood	douglas_	dwarfmor	dwarfpet	easterl1
easterl2	foxglove	freesia	fuchia	gentian

Plants
Botanique
Plantas
Pflanzen

geranium	gladiola	glory	gloxinia	grape_h
grasspin	harebell	hollyhoc	hyacenth	hyacinth
jasmine	lilacs	lilyvall	magnolia	mimosa
mint	narrow	nastur	orchid	orchid2
oregano	oxalis	oxeyedal	pansy	parsley
passionf	periwink	perulily	pinecone	poinsett
primula	redhot	redpoppy	rhododen	rockrose

Plants
Botanique
Plantas
Pflanzen

rose2

rosemary

rosest

rough

sage

scotch

skunkcab

snapdrag

sunflowr

sweethrt

sweetwil

trillium

tulip

violet

wandflow

waterlil

waxplant

wisteria

Reptile
Reptile
Reptil
Reptilie

allgater

lizard1

lizard2

lizard3

lizard4

pangolin

snake1

snake2

snake3

tortois

turtlec

turtles

Reptile
Reptile
Reptil
Reptilie

 TOTEM GRAPHICS

alligato

brontosa

chameleo

cobrat

croc

horntoad

lizard

orintho

plesiosa

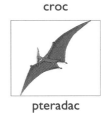

pteradac

ratsnake

seasnake

seaturtl

snapturt

stego

tortoist

treesnak

tricerat

turtleca

tyrannos

anchorc

back2

boat

boat362

cigboat

cruiser

hfoil

hover

j_boat

junk

radarc

sailboat

sailbord

scooner

ship

ship1

ship2

ship3

ship4

skidder

sub1

sub2

symb001

symb002

symb022

symb023

symb038

symb236

symb237

symb238

symb243

symb513

symb526

anchor

anchor1

anchor2

anchor3

anchor4

anchor5

anchor6

anchor7

anchor_1

arleighb

arlghblk

arlghrev

bain

bain_s

battlshp

belknap

blknpblk

blknprev

bnbrgblk

bnbrgrev

bnbridge

boatswn

brkeblk

brkerev

bronstn

brooke

brstnblk

brstnrev

ca_blk

ca_rev

carrier

cfadams

cfadmblk

cfadmrev

cg_cuter

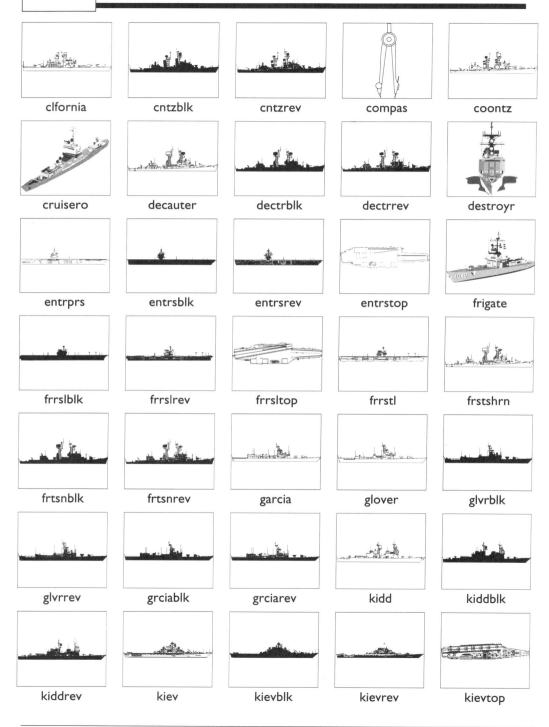

clfornia	cntzblk	cntzrev	compas	coontz
cruisero	decauter	dectrblk	dectrrev	destroyr
entrprs	entrsblk	entrsrev	entrstop	frigate
frrslblk	frrslrev	frrsltop	frrstl	frstshrn
frtsnblk	frtsnrev	garcia	glover	glvrblk
glvrrev	grciablk	grciarev	kidd	kiddblk
kiddrev	kiev	kievblk	kievrev	kievtop

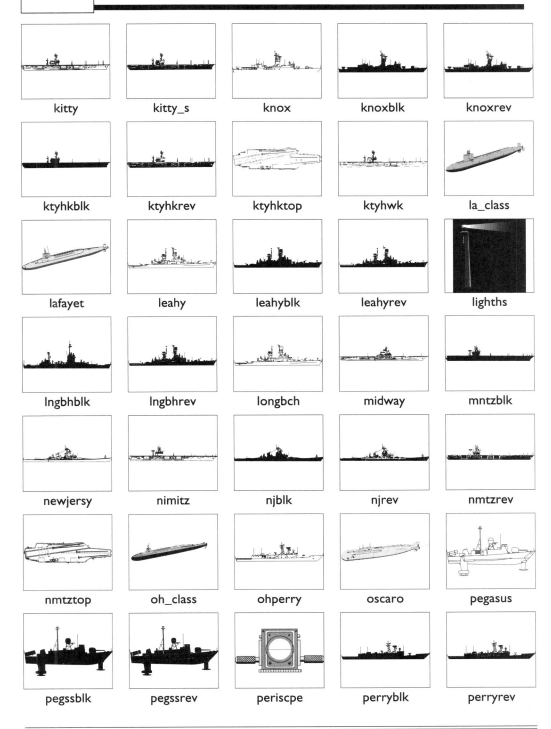

kitty	kitty_s	knox	knoxblk	knoxrev
ktyhkblk	ktyhkrev	ktyhktop	ktyhwk	la_class
lafayet	leahy	leahyblk	leahyrev	lighths
lngbhblk	lngbhrev	longbch	midway	mntzblk
newjersy	nimitz	njblk	njrev	nmtzrev
nmtztop	oh_class	ohperry	oscaro	pegasus
pegssblk	pegssrev	periscpe	perryblk	perryrev

Ship
Bateau
Barco
Schiff

 one mile up inc

seawolf

sprncblk

sprncrev

spruance

sub

tarawa

tcndgblk

tcndgrev

tcndrga

ticon

ticon_s

trawablk

trawarev

truxtun

trxtnblk

trxtnrev

typhoon

us_sub

va_blk

va_rev

virginia

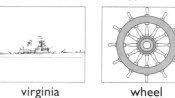
wheel

 Ship
Bateau
Barco
Schiff

 TOTEM GRAPHICS

airboat

anchort

bassboat

bell

block

bowline

canoe

carriert

chock

cleat

cruiset2

cutter

depth

dhelmet

doublehu

ferry

figure

fireboat

freightr

gondola

grounded

hitch

hook

housboat

hydrofo

kayak

knot

lifeboat

lifebuoy

lifejack

lithouse

navigatn

outboard

peri

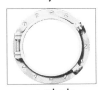
porthole

prop

raceboat

sailbot

sanpan

santamar

Ship
Bateau
Barco
Schiff

scompass

scubat

sextant

slantern

spedboat

sub_1

sub_2

supert

symb600

tug

viking

wheelt

Sign
Panneau
Signos
Schild

Business
Affaires
Negocios
Wirtschaft

blueprnt

briefcas

budget3

bullbear

buscard

chessset

communic

computr

corpjet

coupon

diskbomb

expenses

f_style

festival

flyace

Sign
Panneau
Signos
Schild

Business
Affaires
Negocios
Wirtschaft

handsha3	handwrte	homesad	hrglass	jungloff

laptop	manonrun	manwomn	meeting3	memo3

mf_symb	moneycht	networks	offcesup	ontarget

ontherun	phonemes	phonemsg	phonepad	phonewrk

prodwtch	routslip	sgnmouse	slide3	stopwtch

taxiad	testing	trends

Sign
Panneau
Signos
Schild

Miscellaneous
Divers
Varios
Verschiedenes

angel3

antiques

ballet3

birthday

cheerldr

coffee3

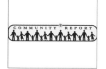
concert

emergcy1

emergcy2

emergcy3

family3

finedine

fitness3

food3

football

geneolgy

gifttag

gourmet

jarlabel

jazz1

jazz2

jazz3

md_sign

menu3

menuinsd

militar3

nametag

newsbear

nosmoke

pencils

penguin

polisci

runner1

runner2

school3

Sign
Panneau
Signos
Schild

Miscellaneous
Divers
Varios
Verschiedenes

techtips

terrorsm

therapy

travel3

winelist

workwomn

Sign
Panneau
Signos
Schild

Icon
Icône
Icono
Sinnbilder

cross01

cross02

cross03

cross04

cross05

cross07

cross09

cross1

cross10

cross14

cross15

cross16

cross17

cross19

cross2

cross20

cross3

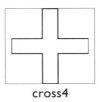
cross4

cross5

cross6

Sign
Panneau
Signos
Schild

Icon
Icône
Icono
Sinnbilder

cross8

symb028

symb034

symb159

symb176

symb177

symb214

symb215

symb216

symb218

symb219

symb220

symb221

symb224

symb230

symb248

symb249

symb251

symb252

symb253

symb255

symb260

symb354

symb360

symb361

symb405

symb406

symb407

symb408

symb409

symb412

symb413

symb430

symb575

symb576

Sign
Panneau
Signos
Schild

Icon
Icône
Icono
Sinnbilder

 COREL

symb577

Sign
Panneau
Signos
Schild

Miscellaneous
Divers
Varios
Verschiedenes

 COREL

aquarius

aries

bigsave

break

cancer

capricrn

clear

cross038

gemini

leo

libra

pisces

s10

s11

s12

s3

sagitars

sale

scorpio

sign01

sign02

sign04

Sign
Panneau
Signos
Schild

Miscellaneous
Divers
Varios
Verschiedenes

sign086

sign087

sign088

sign089

sign090

sign091

sign092

sign093

sign094

sign095

sign096

sign097

sign098

sign099

sign100

sign156

sign157

sign158

sign159

sign160

sign161

sign162

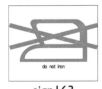

sign163

sign164

sign165

sign166

sign167

sign168

sign169

sign17

sign170

sign171

sign172

sign173

sign174

271

Sign
Panneau
Signos
Schild

Miscellaneous
Divers
Varios
Verschiedenes

sign18

sign197

sign198

sign199

slashed

symaxe

symb083

symb084

symb223

symb225

symb372

symb389

symb390

symb391

symb432

symb565

symcafe

symcoff

symeye

symfaid

symhydr

symsecr

symvend

taurus

virgo

Sign
Panneau
Signos
Schild

Traffic
Signalisation
Traffico
Verkher

2_tracks

fast9

roadsign

s5

sign114

Sign
Panneau
Signos
Schild

Traffic
Signalisation
Traffico
Verkher

sign148

sign149

sign190

sign191

sign192

sign193

sign194

sign195

sign196

sign20

sign200

sign201

sign202

sign203

sign204

sign205

sign206

sign207

sign208

sign209

sign210

sign211

sign212

sign213

sign214

sign215

sign216

sign217

sign218

sign219

sign220

sign221

sign222

sign223

sign224

Sign
Panneau
Signos
Schild

Traffic
Signalisation
Traffico
Verkher

 COREL

sign225

sign226

sign227

sign228

sign229

sign230

sign231

sign232

sign233

sign234

sign235

sign236

sign237

slow8

symbus

Sign
Panneau
Signos
Schild

Warnings
Avertissement
Aviso
Warnungen

 COREL

SEAT BELT
mando01

EYE PROTECTION
mando02

FOOT PROTECTION
mando03

HEAD PROTECTION
mando04

HEARING PROTECTION
mando05

BREATHING
PROTECTION
mando06

WASTE DISPOSAL
mando07

s1

s19

s2

HOT SURFACE
s20

s4

s6

s7

s8

Sign
Panneau
Signos
Schild

Warnings
Avertissement
Aviso
Warnungen

DANGER
NO SMOKING,
MATCHES OR
OPEN LIGHTS

sign001

DANGER
AUTHORIZED
PERSONNEL
ONLY

sign002

DANGER
CONSTRUCTION
AREA

sign003

DANGER
CORROSIVE
MATERIALS

sign004

DANGER
DO NOT CROSS
CONVEYOR

sign005

DANGER
DO NOT
ENTER

sign006

DANGER
DO NOT TOUCH
MACHINES

sign007

DANGER
EYE PROTECTION
REQUIRED

sign008

DANGER
EAR PROTECTION
REQUIRED

sign009

DANGER
ELECTRICAL
HAZARD

sign010

DANGER
FALLING
MATERIAL

sign011

DANGER
FLAMMABLE
LIQUIDS

sign012

DANGER
FLAMMABLE

sign013

DANGER
FLOOR SLIPPERY
WHEN WET

sign014

DANGER
GASOLINE

sign015

DANGER
HARD HAT
AREA

sign016

DANGER
HIGH
VOLTAGE

sign017

DANGER
KEEP
OUT

sign018

DANGER
KEEP GATE
CLOSED

sign019

DANGER
KEEP HANDS
CLEAR

sign020

DANGER
MOVING
MACHINERY

sign021

DANGER
NO
ADMITTANCE

sign022

DANGER
NO
SMOKING

sign023

DANGER
TOXIC
VAPORS

sign024

DANGER
POISON

sign025

DANGER
RESTRICTED
AREA

sign026

DANGER
THIS AREA IS
CLOSED OFF

sign027

DANGER
THIS MACHINE
STARTS
AUTOMATICALLY

sign028

DANGER
EXPLOSIVES

sign029

DANGER
BREATHING MASK
REQUIRED

sign030

CAUTION
CHEMICAL
STORAGE

sign031

CAUTION
DO NOT WALK
ON CONVEYORS

sign032

CAUTION
EAR
PROTECTION
REQUIRED

sign033

CAUTION
EYE
PROTECTION
REQUIRED

sign034

CAUTION
FIRE LANE
KEEP CLEAR
AT ALL TIMES

sign035

Sign
Panneau
Signos
Schild

Warnings
Avertissement
Aviso
Warnungen

 COREL

CAUTION FLAMMABLE LIQUIDS	**CAUTION** FOOT PROTECTION REQUIRED	**CAUTION** HAZARDOUS MATERIAL STORAGE	**CAUTION** HAZARDOUS WASTE STORAGE	**CAUTION** LOW HEAD ROOM
sign036	sign037	sign038	sign039	sign040
CAUTION MEN WORKING ABOVE	**CAUTION** MEN WORKING BELOW	**CAUTION** NO SMOKING BEYOND THIS POINT	**CAUTION** OPEN DOOR SLOWLY	**CAUTION** THIS EQUIPMENT STARTS AND STOPS AUTOMATICALLY
sign041	sign042	sign043	sign044	sign045
CAUTION WATCH YOUR STEP	**CAUTION** DO NOT HANDLE CHEMICALS WITHOUT PROPER PROTECTION	**CAUTION** WET PAINT	**CAUTION** RESPIRATOR REQUIRED BEYOND THIS POINT	**CAUTION** KEEP HANDS CLEAR
sign046	sign047	sign048	sign049	sign050
CAUTION DO NOT TOUCH	**CAUTION** AVOID SKIN CONTACT	**CAUTION** COMPUTER CONTROLLED DO NOT INTERFERE	**CAUTION** DO NOT WEAR JEWELRY OR LOOSE CLOTHING WHEN OPERATING	**CAUTION** THIS DOOR MUST BE KEPT CLOSED
sign051	sign052	sign053	sign054	sign055
SAFETY FIRST KEEP THIS AREA SAFE AND CLEAN	**SAFETY FIRST** KEEP ALL AISLES CLEAR	**SAFETY FIRST** GOGGLES REQUIRED	**SAFETY FIRST** ALL INJURIES NO MATTER HOW SLIGHT MUST BE REPORTED TO YOUR FOREMAN AT ONCE AND BE TREATED AT THE FIRST AID ROOM	**SAFETY FIRST** DO NOT ENTER UNLESS WEARING SAFETY EQUIPMENT
sign056	sign057	sign058	sign059	sign060
SAFETY FIRST DON'T TRY TO LIFT MORE THEN YOU ARE ABLE	**SAFETY FIRST** EYE PROTECTION REQUIRED	**SAFETY FIRST** REPORT ALL UNSAFE CONDITIONS TO YOUR FOREMAN	**SAFETY FIRST** THE SAFE WAY IS THE BEST WAY	**SAFETY FIRST** DON'T TAKE CHANCES
sign061	sign062	sign063	sign064	sign065
SAFETY FIRST CLEAN RESTROOMS MEAN GOOD HEALTH	**SAFETY FIRST** CLEAN UP SPILLS	**SAFETY FIRST** EAR PROTECTION REQUIRED	**SAFETY FIRST** DON'T TAKE CHANCES	**SAFETY FIRST** NO SMOKING
sign066	sign067	sign068	sign069	sign070

Sign
Panneau
Signos
Schild

Warnings
Avertissement
Aviso
Warnungen

NOTICE
ALL VISITORS MUST
GET PASS AT
OFFICE

sign071

NOTICE
AUTHORIZED
PERSONNEL
ONLY

sign072

NOTICE
DO NOT
BLOCK DOOR

sign073

NOTICE
FOOD AND DRINK
PROHIBITED

sign074

NOTICE
HELP KEEP
THIS PLACE
CLEAN

sign075

NOTICE
HARD HATS
MUST BE WORN
IN THIS AREA

sign076

NOTICE
KEEP THIS
PASSAGEWAY
CLEAR

sign077

NOTICE
NO
SMOKING

sign078

NOTICE
NO
LOITERING

sign079

NOTICE
NO
TRESPASSING

sign080

NOTICE
PLEASE WIPE
YOUR FEET

sign081

NOTICE
THESE DOORS MUST
BE KEPT CLOSED

sign082

NOTICE
THE USE OF ALCOHOL
ON THE PREMISES
WILL MEAN IMMEDIATE
DISMISSAL

sign083

NOTICE
EMERGENCY
EXIT

sign084

NOTICE
RESTRICTED AREA
AUTHORIZED
EMPLOYEES ONLY

sign085

sign101

sign102

sign103

sign104

sign105

sign106

sign107

sign108

sign109

sign110

sign111

sign112

sign113

sign115

sign116

sign117

sign118

sign119

sign120

sign121

Sign
Panneau
Signos
Schild

Warnings
Avertissement
Aviso
Warnungen

sign122

sign123

sign124

sign125

sign126

sign127

sign128

sign129

sign130

sign131

sign132

sign133

sign134

sign135

sign136

sign137

sign138

sign139

sign140

sign141

sign142

sign143

sign144

sign145

sign146

sign147

sign15

sign150

sign151

sign152

sign153

sign154

sign155

sign16

sign19

Sign
Panneau
Signos
Schild

symalar

symb217

symb387

symb388

sympois

symshwr

Sign
Panneau
Signos
Schild

church

clrance

cofeetim

crossi

handleft

handrite

hapyhour

hellogal

heloguy1

heloguy2

heloguy3

ladyexpl

loans

movie

oilrig

plant

rsvp

secret

signhold

Sign
Panneau
Signos
Schild

smoking

the_end

theater

wetpaint

wywo

Sign
Panneau
Signos
Schild

aa_grade

action

afassoc

aflogcm2

airforce

amtrak

clasfied

confid

donkeyo

elephant

nardacnr

need2no

nfcu

rad_sym

secreto

top_sec

usaf

1 aid

911

biohazrd

biohz

biohzrd

caduseus

chkup1

chkup2

chkup3

cough

dizzy

elev

eyeprtct

fever

figheart

fpyramid

handsym

hartsymb

icn14

nosmking

nuclmed

pharmacy

poisn

pressure

radat

radation

sniffles

stress

tobacco

wedlike1

wedlike2

wedlike3

Sign
Panneau
Signos
Schild

energy

lemonade

open

opening

salet

sold

wall

Simple Border
Cadres Simples
Marcos Simples
Enfacher Rahmen

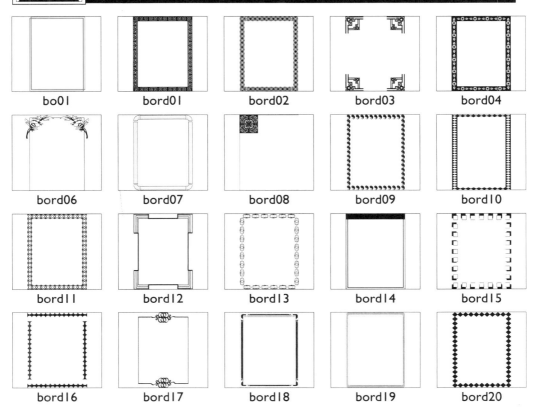

bo01

bord01

bord02

bord03

bord04

bord06

bord07

bord08

bord09

bord10

bord11

bord12

bord13

bord14

bord15

bord16

bord17

bord18

bord19

bord20

Simple Border
Cadres Simples
Marcos Simples
Enfacher Rahmen

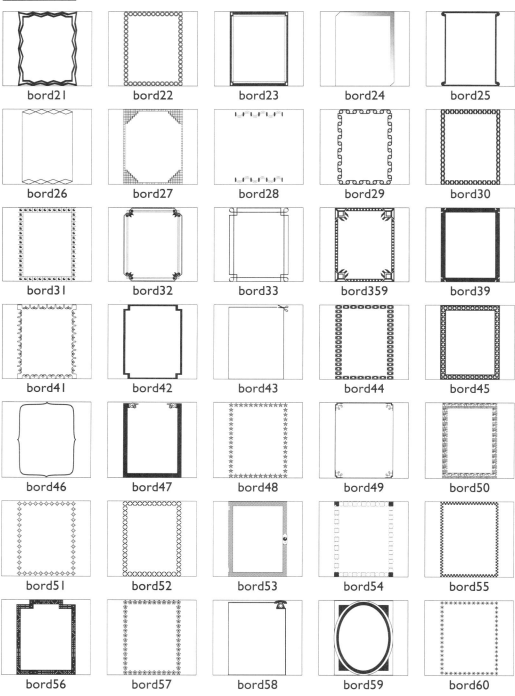

bord21   bord22   bord23   bord24   bord25

bord26   bord27   bord28   bord29   bord30

bord31   bord32   bord33   bord359   bord39

bord41   bord42   bord43   bord44   bord45

bord46   bord47   bord48   bord49   bord50

bord51   bord52   bord53   bord54   bord55

bord56   bord57   bord58   bord59   bord60

Simple Border
Cadres Simples
Marcos Simples
Enfacher Rahmen

COREL

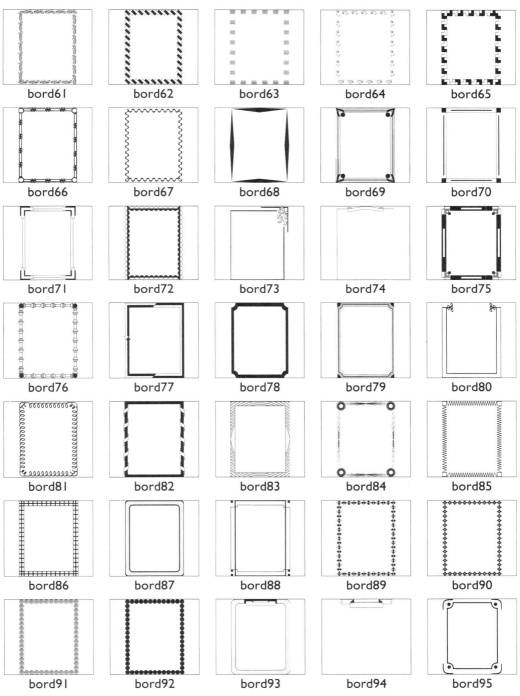

bord61

bord62

bord63

bord64

bord65

bord66

bord67

bord68

bord69

bord70

bord71

bord72

bord73

bord74

bord75

bord76

bord77

bord78

bord79

bord80

bord81

bord82

bord83

bord84

bord85

bord86

bord87

bord88

bord89

bord90

bord91

bord92

bord93

bord94

bord95

Simple Border
Cadres Simples
Marcos Simples
Enfacher Rahmen

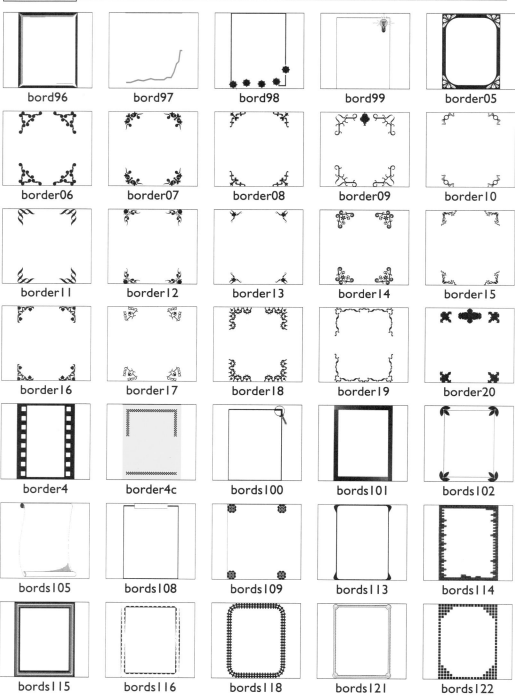

bord96	bord97	bord98	bord99	border05
border06	border07	border08	border09	border10
border11	border12	border13	border14	border15
border16	border17	border18	border19	border20
border4	border4c	bords100	bords101	bords102
bords105	bords108	bords109	bords113	bords114
bords115	bords116	bords118	bords121	bords122

Simple Border
Cadres Simples
Marcos Simples
Enfacher Rahmen

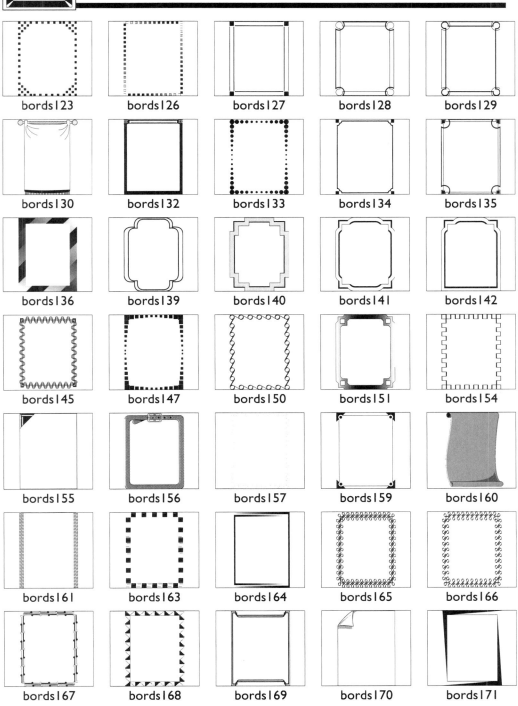

bords123

bords126

bords127

bords128

bords129

bords130

bords132

bords133

bords134

bords135

bords136

bords139

bords140

bords141

bords142

bords145

bords147

bords150

bords151

bords154

bords155

bords156

bords157

bords159

bords160

bords161

bords163

bords164

bords165

bords166

bords167

bords168

bords169

bords170

bords171

Simple Border
Cadres Simples
Marcos Simples
Enfacher Rahmen

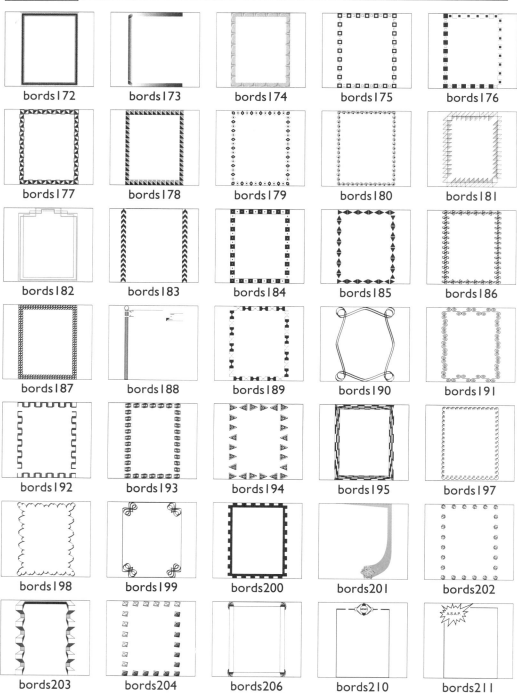

bords172

bords173

bords174

bords175

bords176

bords177

bords178

bords179

bords180

bords181

bords182

bords183

bords184

bords185

bords186

bords187

bords188

bords189

bords190

bords191

bords192

bords193

bords194

bords195

bords197

bords198

bords199

bords200

bords201

bords202

bords203

bords204

bords206

bords210

bords211

Simple Border
Cadres Simples
Marcos Simples
Enfacher Rahmen

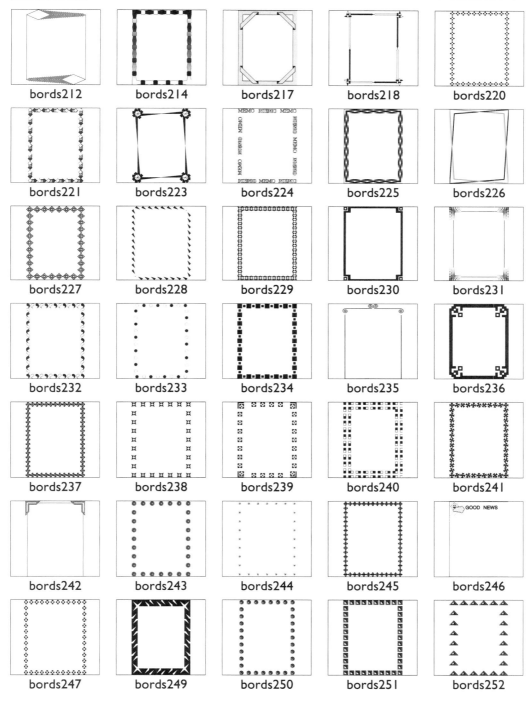

bords212

bords214

bords217

bords218

bords220

bords221

bords223

bords224

bords225

bords226

bords227

bords228

bords229

bords230

bords231

bords232

bords233

bords234

bords235

bords236

bords237

bords238

bords239

bords240

bords241

bords242

bords243

bords244

bords245

bords246

bords247

bords249

bords250

bords251

bords252

Simple Border
Cadres Simples
Marcos Simples
Enfacher Rahmen

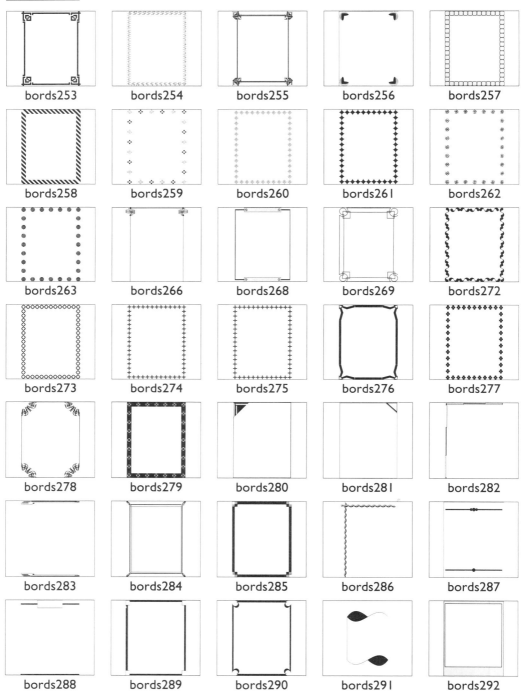

bords253	bords254	bords255	bords256	bords257
bords258	bords259	bords260	bords261	bords262
bords263	bords266	bords268	bords269	bords272
bords273	bords274	bords275	bords276	bords277
bords278	bords279	bords280	bords281	bords282
bords283	bords284	bords285	bords286	bords287
bords288	bords289	bords290	bords291	bords292

Simple Border
Cadres Simples
Marcos Simples
Enfacher Rahmen

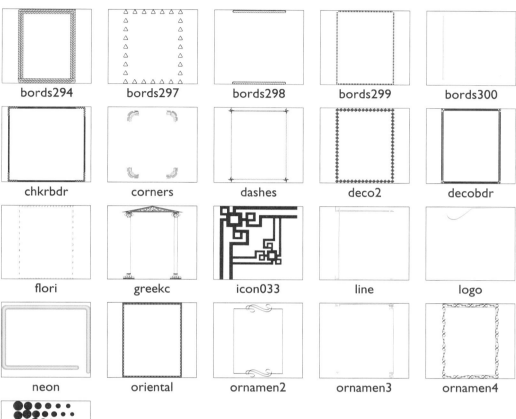

bords294	bords297	bords298	bords299	bords300
chkrbdr	corners	dashes	deco2	decobdr
flori	greekc	icon033	line	logo
neon	oriental	ornamen2	ornamen3	ornamen4
symb533				

Simple Border
Cadres Simples
Marcos Simples
Enfacher Rahmen

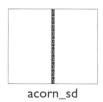

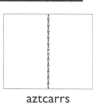

acorn	acorn_sd	acorn_tp	acorn_wr	aztcarrs

Simple Border
Cadres Simples
Marcos Simples
Enfacher Rahmen

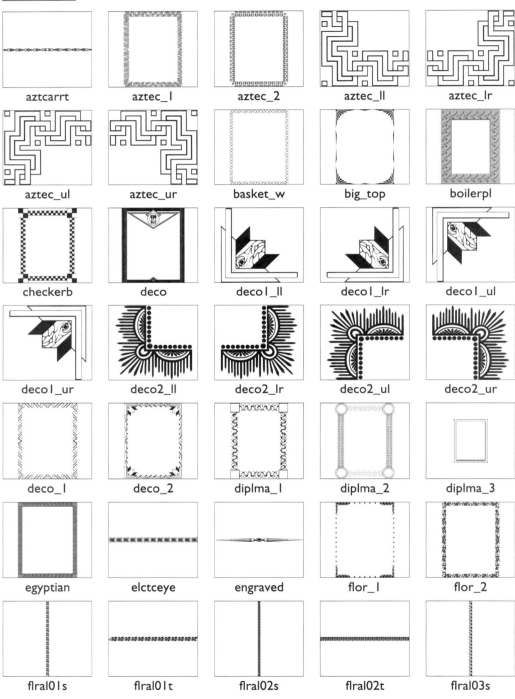

aztcarrt	aztec_l	aztec_2	aztec_ll	aztec_lr
aztec_ul	aztec_ur	basket_w	big_top	boilerpl
checkerb	deco	deco1_ll	deco1_lr	deco1_ul
deco1_ur	deco2_ll	deco2_lr	deco2_ul	deco2_ur
deco_l	deco_2	diplma_l	diplma_2	diplma_3
egyptian	elctceye	engraved	flor_l	flor_2
flral01s	flral01t	flral02s	flral02t	flral03s

Simple Border
Cadres Simples
Marcos Simples
Enfacher Rahmen

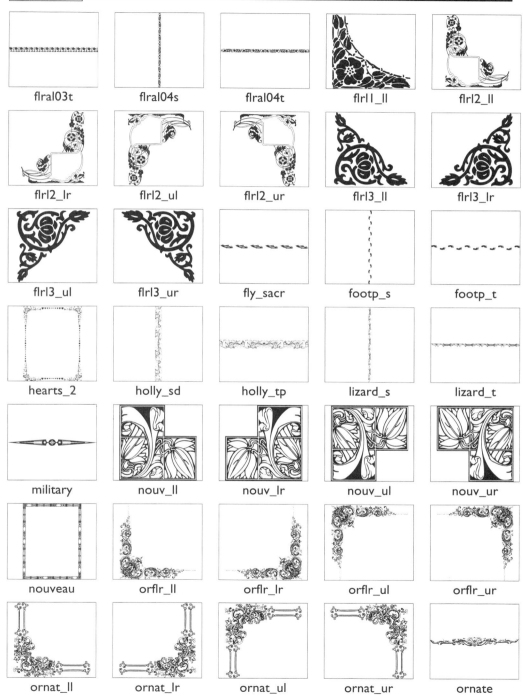

flral03t	flral04s	flral04t	flrl1_ll	flrl2_ll
flrl2_lr	flrl2_ul	flrl2_ur	flrl3_ll	flrl3_lr
flrl3_ul	flrl3_ur	fly_sacr	footp_s	footp_t
hearts_2	holly_sd	holly_tp	lizard_s	lizard_t
military	nouv_ll	nouv_lr	nouv_ul	nouv_ur
nouveau	orflr_ll	orflr_lr	orflr_ul	orflr_ur
ornat_ll	ornat_lr	ornat_ul	ornat_ur	ornate

Simple Border
Cadres Simples
Marcos Simples
Enfacher Rahmen

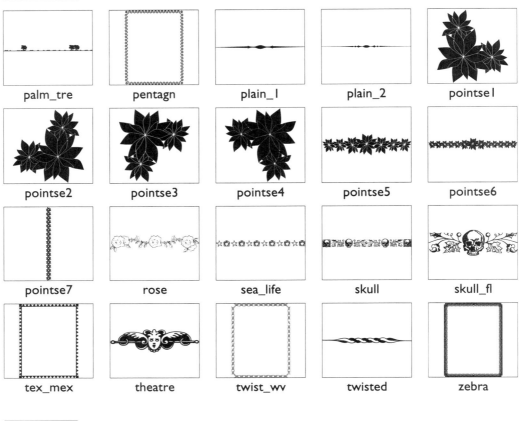

palm_tre	pentagn	plain_I	plain_2	pointseI
pointse2	pointse3	pointse4	pointse5	pointse6
pointse7	rose	sea_life	skull	skull_fl
tex_mex	theatre	twist_wv	twisted	zebra

Simple Border
Cadres Simples
Marcos Simples
Enfacher Rahmen

certI	cert2	cert3	cert4	cert5

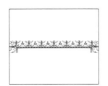
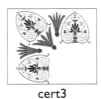

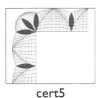

cert6   cert8   cert9

ariane

arneblk

atlasag

atlaso

defsat

dspsat

emu

fltsat

galileo

gpssat

hubble

inflar

magellan

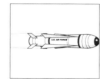

mavrick

milstar

mmu

mmufrt

navstar

nikehur

omv

omvback

para_dsh

polarplt

satllte

sats

saturn

shtl_lch

shtlc_sd

shtlcbot

shtlcveh

shtlicon

shtlopen

Space
Espace
Espacio
Weltall

shtlside

shtltnk

shtltop

shutcfr

shutcsnt

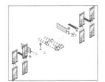

smspasta

spa_shtl

space

spcbeam

spcsta

spstaorb

stbeeng

stmeeng

t3ecent

tealsat

ussrsht

ussrshts

vlss

Sports
Sports
Desportes
Sport

 COREL

bad_raq

badbird

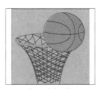

baskball

bball121

bball355

bordjump

bowl350

bowlingc

boxglove

catchbal

Sports
Sports
Desportes
Sport

chinup

curling

darts1

exercise

fball122

footbala

golfbag

golfing

helmets

hockey

pong

sball123

skiboot

skijump

stk_arch

stk_bask

stk_box

stk_cano

stk_cycl

stk_dive

stk_fenc

stk_hock

stk_lift

stk_swim

stk_tenn

stk_watr

symb048

symb169

symb196

symb316

symb317

symb318

symb319

symb320

symb321

Sports
Sports
Desportes
Sport

symb322

symb323

symb324

symb325

symb326

symb327

symb328

symb329

symb330

symb331

symb332

symb333

symb334

symb335

symb336

symb337

symb338

symb339

symb340

symb341

symb342

symb343

symb344

symb345

symb346

symb347

symb348

symb349

symb350

tball354

ten_raq

tenisfem

tenisman

Sports
Sports
Desportes
Sport

badmintn

balncebm

basktbal

batteri

bobsled

boxing

cpleskat

cycling

cyclist

discusi

dwnhlrcr

dwnhlsk

fencingi

fgrskat

footbalc

footbalp

freefall

gymnast l

gymnasti

highjump

hockeyi

hockyi

horsrace

hurdles

javelin

jogging

luge

mntclimb

pairskat

pikedive

pitcheri

pomahors

racqtbal

rings

rowing

runing

shortstp

skieris

skijumpi

slapshot

spedskat

sprinter

surfbord

surfing

swandive

vollybal

watrski l

xcntry

xcntrysk

Sports
Sports
Desportes
Sport

archery

basebalt

baskbalt

bowlingb

boxinggl

croquet

dartst

dogsled

footbalt

ftballhe

glove

golfball

horshoe

pingpngt

strike_

Theme Border
Cadres Thématiques
Marcos
Thematische Rahmen

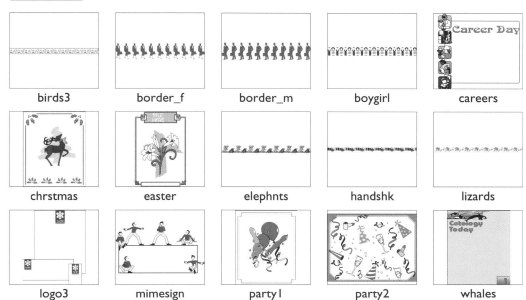

birds3	border_f	border_m	boygirl	careers
chrstmas	easter	elephnts	handshk	lizards
logo3	mimesign	party1	party2	whales

Theme Border
Cadres Thématiques
Marcos
Thematische Rahmen

Animal
Animaux
Animales
Tiere

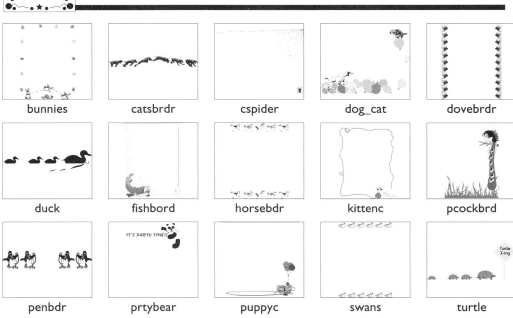

bunnies	catsbrdr	cspider	dog_cat	dovebrdr
duck	fishbord	horsebdr	kittenc	pcockbrd
penbdr	prtybear	puppyc	swans	turtle

Theme Border
Cadres Thématiques
Marcos
Thematische Rahmen

Animal
Animaux
Animales
Tiere

webbordr

Theme Border
Cadres Thématiques
Marcos
Thematische Rahmen

Business
Affaires
Negocios
Wirtschaft

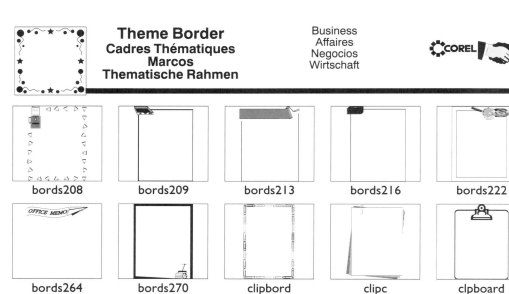

bords208	bords209	bords213	bords216	bords222

bords264	bords270	clipbord	clipc	clpboard

diamnd	emboss2	emboss3	f_pen	flipbrd

forsale2	note_pad	pencbord	penclbdr	phonbord

pinup	scrlbord	slidec	smokefre	stamp1

Theme Border
Cadres Thématiques
Marcos
Thematische Rahmen

Business
Affaires
Negocios
Wirtschaft

timeis

window

Theme Border
Cadres Thématiques
Marcos
Thematische Rahmen

Garden
Jardin
Jardin
Garten

COREL

bamboo

bords162

bushbrd2

cherybrd

fleurdli

flowersc

geomflwr

leaves

oasis

plantbrd

tulipsc

vinebdr

weedbord

Theme Border
Cadres Thématiques
Marcos
Thematische Rahmen

Holiday
Festivités
Festivo
Feiertage

balloons

bday

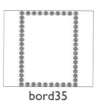
bord34

bord35

bord360

bord38

bords117

bords148

bords152

bords248

bubble1

christma

frenchh

holiday

monkey_b

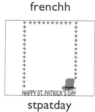
postcard

shower

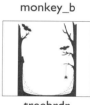
stpatday

thanksgv

treebrdr

xmas

xmas026

Theme Border
Cadres Thématiques
Marcos
Thematische Rahmen

Leisure
Loisirs
Ocio
Freizeit

ballet

basketbl

bbalbrdr

bords112

bords124

Theme Border
Cadres Thématiques
Marcos
Thematische Rahmen

Leisure
Loisirs
Ocio
Freizeit

bords125

bowling1

brushc

casinod

crswrd

dancbord

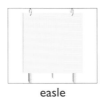

dsertbrd

easle

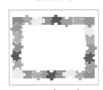

jrsybrdr

puzcbord

puzzbord

rinkbrdr

rollers

soccer

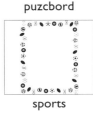

sports

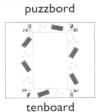

tenboard

volyball

Theme Border
Cadres Thématiques
Marcos
Thematische Rahmen

Miscellaneous
Divers
Varios
Verschiedenes

arrows

bluribon

bo09

boardc

bord05

bord36

bord361

bord37

bord40

bords103

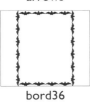

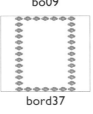

Theme Border
Cadres Thématiques
Marcos
Thematische Rahmen

Miscellaneous
Divers
Varios
Verschiedenes

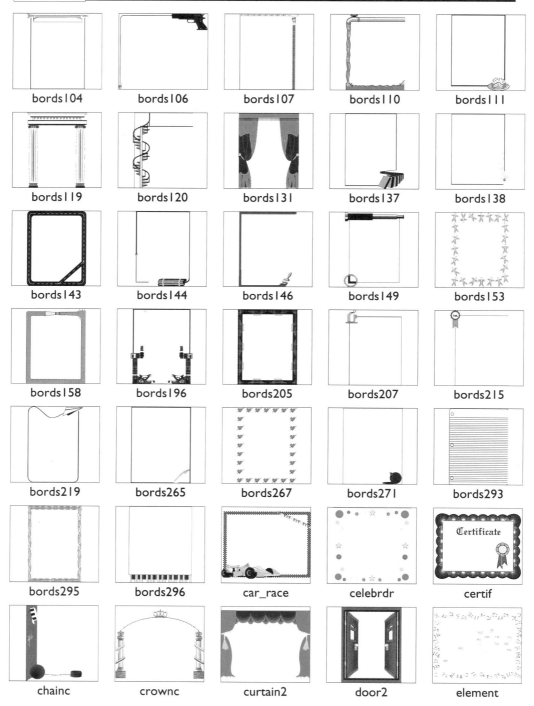

bords104

bords106

bords107

bords110

bords111

bords119

bords120

bords131

bords137

bords138

bords143

bords144

bords146

bords149

bords153

bords158

bords196

bords205

bords207

bords215

bords219

bords265

bords267

bords271

bords293

bords295

bords296

car_race

celebrdr

certif

chainc

crownc

curtain2

door2

element

Theme Border
Cadres Thématiques
Marcos
Thematische Rahmen

Miscellaneous
Divers
Varios
Verschiedenes

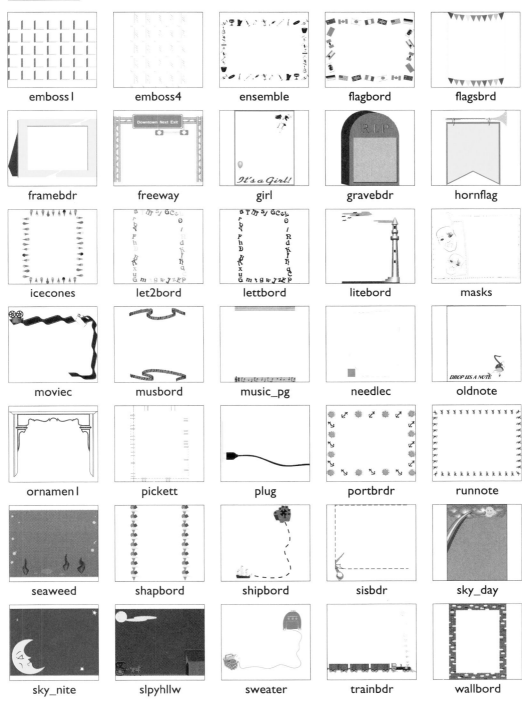

emboss1	emboss4	ensemble	flagbord	flagsbrd
framebdr	freeway	girl	gravebdr	hornflag
icecones	let2bord	lettbord	litebord	masks
moviec	musbord	music_pg	needlec	oldnote
ornamen1	pickett	plug	portbrdr	runnote
seaweed	shapbord	shipbord	sisbdr	sky_day
sky_nite	slpyhllw	sweater	trainbdr	wallbord

Theme Border
Cadres Thématiques
Marcos
Thematische Rahmen

wind2

zambonib

Theme Border
Cadres Thématiques
Marcos
Thematische Rahmen

animal

baby_toy

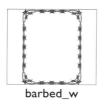

barbed_w

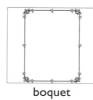

boquet

btrflyll

btrflylr

btrflyul

btrflyur

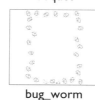

bug_worm

candycn1

candycn2

candycn3

candycn4

candyhor

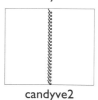

candyve2

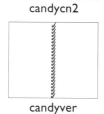

candyver

chefspec

chrb_ll

chrb_lr

chrb_ul

chrb_ur

chrbl_ll

chrbl_lr

dancfish

drama

Theme Border
Cadres Thématiques
Marcos
Thematische Rahmen

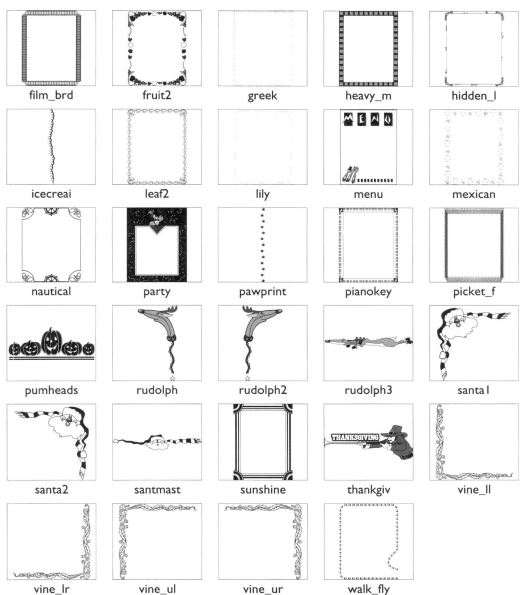

film_brd	fruit2	greek	heavy_m	hidden_l
icecreai	leaf2	lily	menu	mexican
nautical	party	pawprint	pianokey	picket_f
pumheads	rudolph	rudolph2	rudolph3	santa1
santa2	santmast	sunshine	thankgiv	vine_ll
vine_lr	vine_ul	vine_ur	walk_fly	

Theme Border
Cadres Thématiques
Marcos
Thematische Rahmen

Animal
Animaux
Animales
Tiere

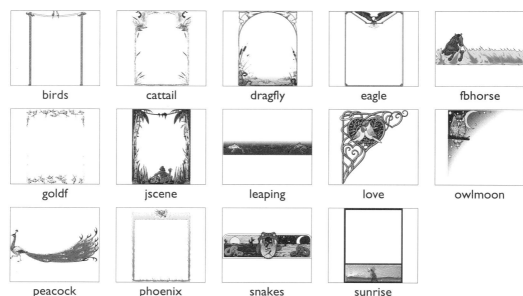

birds	cattail	dragfly	eagle	fbhorse
goldf	jscene	leaping	love	owlmoon
peacock	phoenix	snakes	sunrise	

Theme Border
Cadres Thématiques
Marcos
Thematische Rahmen

Garden
Jardin
Jardin
Garten

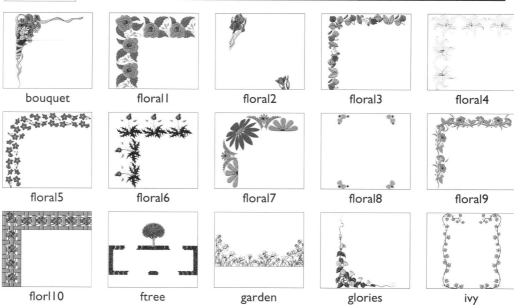

bouquet	floral1	floral2	floral3	floral4
floral5	floral6	floral7	floral8	floral9
florl10	ftree	garden	glories	ivy

Theme Border
Cadres Thématiques
Marcos
Thematische Rahmen

Garden
Jardin
Jardin
Garten

log

roses

spruce

thistle

vines

wlilies

Theme Border
Cadres Thématiques
Marcos
Thematische Rahmen

Holiday
Festivités
Festivo
Feiertage

candles

copia

hollyb

mistleto

sleigh

wedding

witchb

Theme Border
Cadres Thématiques
Marcos
Thematische Rahmen

Miscellaneous
Divers
Varios
Verschiedenes

arches

cert10

chariot

cliff

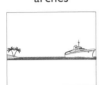
comet

cruiset

dramat

fall

kites

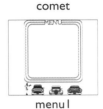
menu1

menu2

milky

oship

ropes

sailing

steep

torches

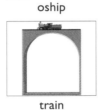
train

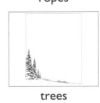
trees

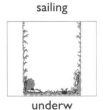
underw

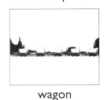
wagon

windg

windp

Theme Border
Cadres Thématiques
Marcos
Thematische Rahmen

People
Gens
Gente
Leute

alad

angelt2

bathing

brand

cannibal

Theme Border
Cadres Thématiques
Marcos
Thematische Rahmen

cherub

chief

creation

dancer

fairy

flutep

goddess

hair

harp

mariner

merm

mother

pioneer

shep

smelling

string

strong

Tools
Outils
Herramientas
Werkzeuge

COREL

bandsaw

circsaw

drill

grind073

jigsawc

meastape

routerc

ruler

symb047

symb138	symb140	symb142	symb143	symb144
symb145	symb146	symb147	symb148	symb149
symb150	symb151	symb152	symb153	symb154
symb155	symb156	symb157	symb197	symb198
symb199	symb209	symb212	symb359	symb401
symb481	symb535	symb562	symb563	symb564

thread

Tools
Outils
Herramientas
Werkzeuge

chaini

hammeri2

ladder

monkrech

paintbrs

screw

wrench

Tools
Outils
Herramientas
Werkzeuge

adjustsq

allenwre

anvil

backsaw

bellows

bowsaw

box_endw

brush

c_clamp

carraigb

cement

chainhoo

chainsaw

chaint

chalklin

chisel

circusaw

compass

cork

cotter

Tools
Outils
Herramientas
Werkzeuge

crescent

crosscut

dividers

drillbit

drilpres

dustpan

elecsand

electric

filet

floorjac

framing

gluegun

grease

hacksaw

hammert

handplan

handtruc

hatchet

hexbolt

hoe

hose

jack

jigsaw

lagbolt

lawnrake

lockwash

mallet

micromet

needle_n

nuts

pick

pliers

protract

prybar

punch

putknife

rake

razorkni

ripsaw

router

rulert

sharpen

shears

shovel

sledge

socket

soldgun

soldiron

spring

standard

stapler2

t_square

tablesaw

tap

tapemeas

tire

triangle

troublit

trowel

turnbuck

umbrella

vice

visegrps

whisk

wirebrus

wirecon1

wirecon2

woodchis

xacto

316

Car
Voiture
Cochex
Auto

1953_vet

300zx

328

32cryco

35ford

36pontia

500sl

51desoto

535

55cryco

57t_bird

69f_bird

87vette

accura

allante

backvett

benz

bikefem

bronco

broncoii

bugg

cabrolet

cadfleet

car1

car364

car365

car366

car367

celica

chevtruk

colt100d

colt100e

convette

cooper

Vehicle
Véhicule
Véhiculo
Fahrzeuge

Car
Voiture
Cochex
Auto

corsica

corvette

crashc

crx

cutlass

daytona

elfc

euro

excel

f150

formula1

fuego

gm_toy

j4 × 4

k_car

lambo1

lambo2

lemans01

lemans02

linclimo

lincolnc

lx

lynx

markvii

mga

micra

mustang

newyorkr

nikki

oldcar1

oldcar2

oldcar4

oldcar6

penski

peugt205

Vehicle
Véhicule
Véhiculo
Fahrzeuge

Car
Voiture
Cochex
Auto

piazza

police

porsche1

porsche2

porsche3

porsche4

porsche5

pulsar

quatro

race368

race369

rollz

rx7

rx_7a

saxon

sentra

shelby

spider

ss

subaru

t_bird1

t_bird2

taurusc

taxi01

taxi02

testa

vette1

volvo1

volvo2

volvo3

xj12

xj6

xjs

Vehicle
Véhicule
Véhiculo
Fahrzeuge

Icon
Icône
Icono
Sinnbild

symb003

symb004

symb008

symb009

symb010

symb012

symb014

symb017

symb049

symb091

symb231

symb233

symb234

symb235

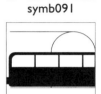

symb239

symb240

symb244

symb245

symb246

symb247

symb315

symb500

symb501

symb502

symb503

symb504

symb505

symb506

symb507

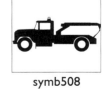

symb508

symb510

symb511

symb512

Vehicle
Véhicule
Véhiculo
Fahrzeuge

Miscellaneous
Divers
Varios
Verschiedenes

1jason

bicyclec

bike

bike370

bike390

bodyman

carradio

choochoo

ducati

flyermc

gasnozzl

gaspumpa

gaspumpc

helmetc

hondwing

jetski

katana

lambike

loader

moped

mv1

mv2

mv3

mv4

rad

raser

skeedoo1

skeedoo2

spkplug

symb015

symb516

tank01

tank02

Vehicle
Véhicule
Véhiculo
Fahrzeuge

Miscellaneous
Divers
Varios
Verschiedenes

tank03

tank04

tank05

tank06

tank07

tank08

tractor3

trailbik

train248

trainc

Vehicle
Véhicule
Véhiculo
Fahrzeuge

Truck
Camion
Camión
LKW

amblance

astro

bus

buss

cabtruck

cubevan

dumptruk

econobox

forklifa

heavytug

lifttruk

lightug

lofttruk

mixer

monster

mover

mpv

nistruck

pathfind

Vehicle
Véhicule
Véhiculo
Fahrzeuge

Truck
Camion
Camión
LKW

ranger

samuri

skoolbus

snowplow

snowtrek

st_plow

symb509

tanker

towtruck

toytruck

trailerc

truck01

whitegmc

xcavator

Vehicle
Véhicule
Véhiculo
Fahrzeuge

busi

cara

crane

helicopt

pickup

scholbus

semi

sportcar

taxidriv

truck

Vehicle
Véhicule
Véhiculo
Fahrzeuge

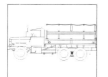
2ton

hemett

hmmamb

hmmsqd

hmmtow

hmmwvtow

mil_4×4

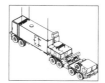
mob_cmdt

r2ton

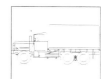
shopvan

trailer

trailero

traino

trk_trn

truck1

truck2

truck3

Vehicle
Véhicule
Véhiculo
Fahrzeuge

ambulanc

atvrace

bigwheel

carriage

crashed

decker

fedext

forklift

j4×4t

jet

Vehicle
Véhicule
Véhiculo
Fahrzeuge

jet747

quad

racecar

racecar2

sanfran

snowmob

ups

Weapon
Armes
Arma
Waffe

aavside

agm_69a

agm_78ar

agm_84a

aim_120a

aim_7m

aim_9sid

aim_sprw

air_mssl

airtoair

ak47

alert

am39

antisub

apc1

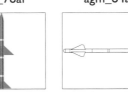

apc2

apc3

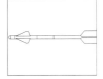

apc5

apc6

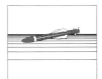

appcamo

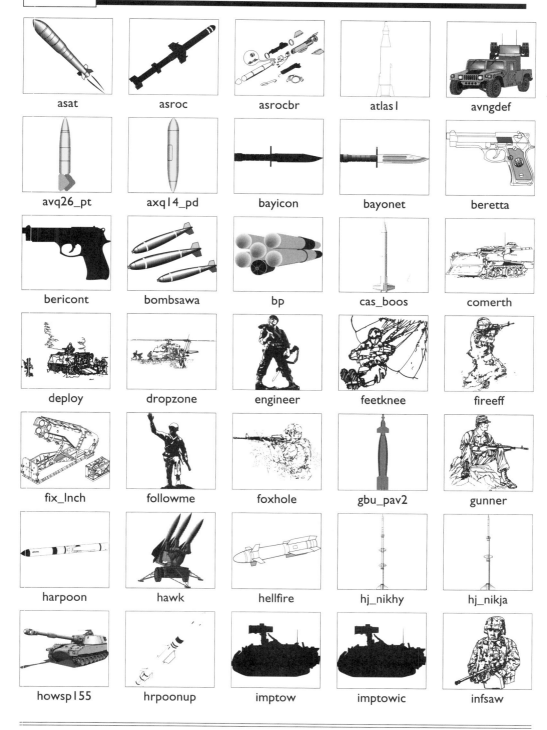

asat   asroc   asrocbr   atlas1   avngdef

avq26_pt   axq14_pd   bayicon   bayonet   beretta

bericont   bombsawa   bp   cas_boos   comerth

deploy   dropzone   engineer   feetknee   fireeff

fix_Inch   followme   foxhole   gbu_pav2   gunner

harpoon   hawk   hellfire   hj_nikhy   hj_nikja

howsp155   hrpoonup   imptow   imptowic   infsaw

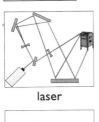
laser

launcher

lav

lavwater

lmine

m106

m113a1

m113acav

m119105

m132

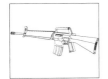
m16

m16o

m16simp

m16sold

m1_tank

m1detail

m1moving

m224

m249auto

m2assa

m2fight

m2fr

m2ifv

m2move

m2rear

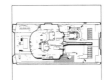
m2top

m48ada

m548

m551tank

m577a1

m60

m60a3

m88a1

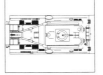
m88a1top

m901itoe

Weapon
Armes
Arma
Waffe

m9acom	min_ares	mirv	mk193	mk46
mk83_bmb	mlrs	mob_lnch	mopp4	mortarl
nik_nik	nuke_b61	patriot	phalanx	prone
rapelc	rplhel	scimitar	scud	sgt_boos
sgunner	sidewind	sm1	soldier	soldm203
starbird	stinger	stnglnch	sword	t72
talos_ca	talos_hy	taskfrc	tomahawk	trident

Weapon
Armes
Arma
Waffe

vlasroc

xtrident

Weather
Météo
Tiempo
Wetter

cloud063

cold217

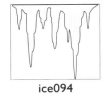

ice094

rain064

raingirl

snow025

splat096

sun062

symb037

symb373

symb377

symb556

symb557

symb558

symb567

symb568

symb569

symb570

symb571

symb572

symb573

symb574

umbrelaa

Woman
Femme
Muyer
Frau

bookfem1

bookfem2

compfem1

compfem2

compfem3

deskfem1

deskfem2

fempose1

fempose2

flipchrt

lettrfem

office2

on_phone

pagefem

phonefem

proofred

readfem1

readfem2

readfem3

readprnt

spywomen

stndfem1

work210

work211

workfem4

Woman
Femme
Muyer
Frau

Historical
Histoire
Histórico
Geschichte

borgia11

cleopat

madcurie

peron_e1

queensco

qvictor

Woman
Femme
Muyer
Frau

Humor
Humor
Humorismo
Humor

face115

face116

hero306

hero307

hero308

humor151

humor155

humor156

humor193

humor216

humor240

humor278

humor314

point186

read146

run225

vtory184

work261

Woman
Femme
Muyer
Frau

Icon
Icônes
Icono
Sinnbilder

busstop

bxwface1

dancerc1

faceside

jumper3

kickingc

ladyf

medea

portphon

posefem1

posefem2

reading4

reading5

running2

shoping

shopper

skiprope

symb261

symb262

symb264

symb265

symb266

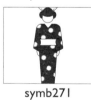

symb271

symb273

symb274

symb276

symb277

symb278

symb279

symb280

symb281

symb307

symb381

symb382

Woman
Femme
Muyer
Frau

Icon
Icônes
Icono
Sinnbilder

symb383

symb384

symb434

symb435

symb436

symb437

symb438

symb439

vactn383

waitress

walking1

walking3

Woman
Femme
Muyer
Frau

Miscellaneous
Divers
Varios
Verschiedenes

basktfem

bride

bxwface3

bxwface4

cake311

cofee265

coffefem

crouch1

crouch2

dance305

dance380

doctorc

dorwyfem

drawgirl

eatfem

Woman
Femme
Muyer
Frau

Miscellaneous
Divers
Varios
Verschiedenes

face

face117

faceback

facefem

facefrnt

fashface

fem_chr

fem_fash

fem_shoe

femdoctr

femnurse

femwplan

flirt197

fmdesign

grad381

hostess

image02

image02b

jrobrts2

kickfem

laughfem

monalsa1

monalsa2

nurse291

nwmadona

okshoper

onporch

phone195

pose242

quickfem

royalook

school

seatfem1

seatfem2

seatfem3

Woman
Femme
Muyer
Frau

Miscellaneous
Divers
Varios
Verschiedenes

seatfem4

seatfem5

serve246

singr264

sit241

stndfem2

stndfem3

stndfem4

studyfem

tablefem

takeout

telegirl

telgirl3

towelfem

vactn384

wait275

waitres

walkfem1

walkfem2

walkfem3

waterfem

Woman
Femme
Muyer
Frau

Sports
Sports
Desportes
Sport

carryfem

climbfem

dancerc2

exrse398

exrse399

Woman
Femme
Muyer
Frau

Sports
Sports
Desportes
Sport

exrse400

fem_ten

finish

horsefem

juggler

mntbike

runerfem

surfer

swimsuit

tenis397

Woman
Femme
Muyer
Frau

Business
Affaires
Negocios
Wirtschaft

buswoman

busygirl

candlei

fly_fngr

hon_bwmn

meet_gal

missphon

portfoli

r_est_sd

r_est_sl

wtrclskl

Woman
Femme
Muyer
Frau

Entertainment
Spectacles
Diversión
Underhaltung

cheri

dollyi

liz_tylr

madoni l

oprah_w

p_abdul

partyldy

Woman
Femme
Muyer
Frau

Humor
Humor
Humorismo
Humor

battlaxe

btyqeen

cowgirl

fly_womn

gabby

good_gal

ladytalk

madworld

nag

nursei

retl_gal

secretry

secrtry

trainer

Woman
Femme
Muyer
Frau

Icon
Icônes
Icono
Sinnbilder

bathrobe

fashioni

graduat

grocries

laundryi

umbrela

withbook

woman

Woman
Femme
Muyer
Frau

Miscellaneous
Divers
Varios
Verschiedenes

africai

awardwom

bikini

bridei

bt_davis

cocktail

dianai

fitness

holland

j_of_arc

j_onasis

k_hepbrn

lady

m_monroe

madonni2

model

paintri4

paris

queen

recption

Woman
Femme
Muyer
Frau

Miscellaneous
Divers
Varios
Verschiedenes

ret_clth

sec_papr

shopspre

shshoper

sportcai

surprldy

teacher

thankgal

thatcher

theresa

typing

vanity

waitrsc1

watrski2

witchi

workout

Woman
Femme
Muyer
Frau

afemf

blindsit

cook

d911

docf

exercise

eyetest

fcrutch

fdoctor

female

Woman
Femme
Muyer
Frau

femdent

files

headach1

lfemf

nurse

nursf

paraf

polf

recept

smilpers

tothsmil

xray

Woman
Femme
Muyer
Frau

Business
Affaires
Negocios
Wirtschaft

b_woman1

b_woman2

dataentr

model_2

running

sales

stewrdes

typist

Woman
Femme
Muyer
Frau

Entertainment
Spectacles
Diversión
Underhaltung

actres_l

actress2

balletd2

balletda

belly

bette

chert

dollyt

flamenco

liz

lucy

marilyn

raquel

showgirl

vanna

Woman
Femme
Muyer
Frau

Miscellaneous
Divers
Varios
Verschiedenes

angry

anniverl

artist2

artnouvj

bag

blackwom

cleopatr

construc

cookt

cowgirlt

devilwom

dresser

eskimo

fmodell

fmodel2

Woman
Femme
Muyer
Frau

Miscellaneous
Divers
Varios
Verschiedenes

fmodel3

fmodel4

fmodel5

fmodel6

fmodel7

fmodel8

godiva

graduate

hammock

happy

hottub

hula

japanese

japdance

japfan

japhat

japlant

japminst

japmirr

jappara

japread

libertyw

library

madonnt

maid

manicure

missamer

model_1

model_3

model_4

model_5

model_6

monalisa

nude

nude_1

Woman
Femme
Muyer
Frau

Miscellaneous
Divers
Varios
Verschiedenes

nun

nurset

operator

opsinger

persian

playboy

pregnant

princesd

queent

reporter

seams

senior

suitcase

sunbath

supermom

tahitian

teachert

thaidanc

thatchrt

venus

waitrsst

womando

yardwork

Woman
Femme
Muyer
Frau

Sports
Sports
Desportes
Sport

barrelra

cheer

gymnast

jogger

rider

Woman
Femme
Muyer
Frau

Sports
Sports
Desportes
Sport

roller

scuba

situps

skater

tennispl

volley